Chalk Stream Reflections

Walking the Rivers of Hertfordshire

For Beck,

Not suggesting that you come and
tick each watercourse, but just
to give you a flavour of
your ancestral county.

TIM HAGYARD

Peter.

This book is dedicated to all the wildlife,
environmental and citizen scientists and volunteers
of Hertfordshire, England and the world over
who campaign and toil in uncertainty
for healthy rivers and
a better world.

Chalk Stream Reflections

Copyright © 2023 Tim Hagyard
By Mindful Steps Publishing
https://mindfulstepspublishing.wordpress.com

First edition July 2023

Sketches from *Wind in the Willows* 1984 Purnell Publishing are by Val Biro illustrator.

ISBN: Paperback: 978-1-8380782-2-5
ISBN eBook: 978-1-8380782-3-2

A CIP catalogue record for this book is available from the British Library.

Cover and interior design Andy Meaden www.meadencreative.com

Footpath maps are published using OS information.
© Crown copyright and database rights 2023 OS AC0000862788

Contents

List of Figures / Maps / Photos

Rivers of Hertfordshire

Maps of suggested additional footpath links

Walk Photographs

Introduction

Water Flows, Life is Given,
Rises from Earth, Falls from Heaven,
Water Flowing So We Sing,
Bless The Holy Spring.

– **Will Parsons, pilgrim**[1]

Over the summer of 2020, I walked all the rivers and waterways of Hertfordshire – a total of about 350 miles. Long walks affect us in unanticipated ways. Memories of our ramblings surface in later everyday moments, prompted by work, conversation or news items. We reflect and the ground shifts; perspectives aren't what they were. This is what happened to me, and what motivated me to write this book.

In part, the walk was to get to know Hertfordshire better.[2] I was working for CPRE, The Countryside Charity, at the time. The initial trigger was a shared sponsored walk with the Amos Trust, to protest Israel's then proposed annexation of the Jordan Valley. In 2017, I was one of a group who walked five months and 2,000 miles to Palestine from London. That's another story[3] – but I recall seeing many depleted and dried-up rivers across Europe, as well as the extreme depletion of the Jordan river, reduced to only 5% of its historic flow. I realised then that we need a

....

1   See http://wayfaringbritain.com
2   Another option would have been the 195-mile Hertfordshire Way. Guide Book from Friends of the Hertfordshire Way https://www.fhw.org.uk/
3   Tim Hagyard, *Mindful Steps for Palestine*. Mindful Steps Publishing, 2020. https://mindfulstepspublishing.wordpress.com

cultural shift, because water shortages and water conservation are urgent international issues.[4] And as the saying goes, 'Think globally, but act locally' – so here I'm looking closely at water-stressed Hertfordshire.

In England, the public's greater engagement with rivers during the Covid pandemic of 2020 was a reminder that we are instinctively drawn to water. Both science and all the world's great faiths teach that water is the very essence of life. Our own bodies are 60% water. The reason space scientists search for water on Mars is they know it is the key to life itself. It's the same for our 'Planet Water', although we named it 'Earth'. We forget this at our peril.

'We never know the worth of water till the well is dry'

(Thomas Fuller, seventeenth-century preacher)

Hertfordshire and England's chalk streams are globally rare, a gentle, unassuming but uniquely English gift to global ecology. They're as English as *The Wind in the Willows*. Rain falls on the high chalk downs, soaks into the topsoil and permeable chalk, is naturally filtered and purified by its geological layers, and finally emerges mineral-rich, alkaline and at a steady year-round temperature and flow. Perfect properties for a unique stable flow ecosystem. The exposed chalk ridge (Fig. 1), once the seabed millions of years ago when Britain and Hertfordshire were submerged, is found only in this corner of England and a small area of northern France, unlike anywhere else in the world. Hertfordshire has 10% and England 85% of the world's 300 chalk streams. They are our tropical rainforests and worthy of far greater love and respect than we currently show them.

....

4   Fred Pearce, *When the Rivers Run Dry: The Global Water Crisis and How to Solve It.* Granta Publications, 2018.

Figure 1. Chalk Outcrops and the Rivers of Britain

Map contains OS data (c) Crown copyright 2023

Classically, a chalk stream is a meandering body of crystal-clear water, crossing sharp gravel beds amidst long trails of water plants in wide flood meadows. The clear water of the chalk aquifer allows for good light penetration, steady conditions and minerals such as calcium and magnesium: a niche habitat for a rich range of plants and species such as water vole, brown trout and crayfish. Water takes a long time to drain down to the aquifer, a natural store that doesn't evaporate, and so winter rainfall can maintain summer flows. The seasonal variation gives rise to ephemeral winterbournes at headwaters.

However, as most people know, our chalk streams face a number of threats including over-abstraction, pollution and climate change. Almost all Hertfordshire's water supply comes from the chalk aquifer, the same aquifer that feeds the chalk streams, so over-abstraction for domestic or commercial use means the rivers suffer in both quantity and quality.

Seeing old mills on the rivers was a reminder of how people once harnessed their power. Towns such as St Albans and Ware grew by the navigation of the Lea and the Ver. Over centuries human interventions widened, straightened, drained and dredged the river landscape, disrupting the ecological balance. It also created a system of canals and locks with all the pleasures they offer in boating and living on water. The most troubling aspect of my walk, to a non-expert eye, was the evident stagnation, rubbish, dried-up riverbeds and pollution. I witnessed blue-green algal blooms and nutrient-rich froth. Why and how could this be happening?

Public concern about rivers has been around for years, but mostly sporadic and localised – for instance, when the Ver in St Albans disappeared during the drought of 1976. In the last few years, it has come to the fore with evidence of worsening standards, private profiteering, and regulatory and government failure. Less publicised but related to this is our profligate and wasteful use of water. It's an outdated attitude, fortunately in retreat, that our planet is one of infinite resource. Watching the magical river scenes in the *Gone Fishing* TV series brought my attention to the river campaigning of Feargal Sharkey, resident of Hertfordshire, who appeared in one episode on the river Lea. I subsequently learned of many other campaigns such as River Action UK[5], Watershed.[6] and Stormwater Shepherds[7]

Many current environmental issues are part of a wider international pattern of excess consumption and exploitation. Vested interests, negligence and wishful thinking play too great a role in the politics of decision-making. England's chalk aquifers are being overexploited, as are aquifers beneath the Saudi desert and the Arizona in the USA. Hertfordshire's chalk streams are drying up, as are mighty rivers like the Rio Grande, the Yangtze and the Po, reduced to historic lows. It is estimated that globally 773 million people live in water-stressed areas.[8] Latest Environment Agency maps (Fig. 2) now designate the whole of central and southern England as 'water stressed'.[9]

....

5   River Action UK, established 2021. Sign their petition and read their Charter for Rivers https://riveractionuk.com/
6   Watershed. *Independent investigative journalism* by Rachel Salvidge and Leana Hosea http://watershedinvestigations.com/about-us/
7   Stormwater Shepherds. *For clean water free of plastic and urban pollution.* https://www.stormwatershepherds.org.uk/
8   Taikan Oki, 'Water Shortages', in Greta Thunberg (ed.), *The Climate Book.* Allen Lane, 2023.
9   Environment Agency, *Updating the Determination of Water Stressed Areas in England*, July 2021. https://consult.environment-agency.gov.uk/environment-and-business/updating-the-determination-of-water-stressed-areas/.

Figure 2. Water Stressed Areas. July 2021

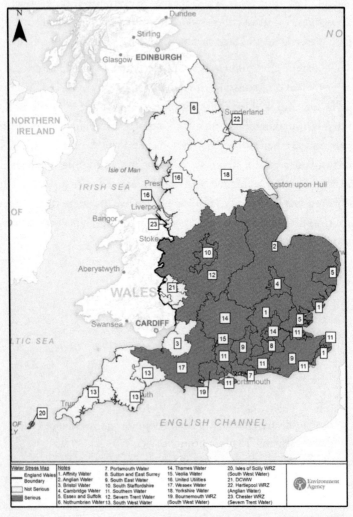

(c) Environment Agency, 2021. Contains public sector information licensed under the Open Government Licence v3.0.

Farming practices and a post-war legacy of heavy fertiliser and chemical use is another major issue. Nitrates and phosphates can filter down to the chalk aquifers and it may take decades for these to recover, even if all fertiliser use were to cease tomorrow. Domestic use includes perplexing inconsistencies. Consider that every year millions of litres of untreated sewage are spilled from 'treatment works', destroying wildlife and threatening public health. Meanwhile, expensively processed drinkable quality water is piped into our homes and a third of this is flushed down the toilet.

My walk through Hertfordshire made me more conscious of local water scarcity, so I experimented with my own water use over two years, with a focus on greywater recycling. Ken Livingstone, ex-Mayor of London, challenged conventions when he encouraged Londoners to save water and flush selectively – 'let the yellow mellow'. Of course, the system suffers from leaks, underinvestment, road run-off and farming pollution which all have to be tackled too, but with accelerating climate change and more extreme patterns of rainfall, it is hugely important to adapt. We need to see high-consumption habits for the pollution that they are. Over-abstraction leads to low river flows which concentrates pollutants and choking sediment, and lowers the amounts of dissolved oxygen that supports aquatic life.

In England and Wales, though not Scotland, we have the widely disliked privatised water companies. Huge profits accumulate, bonus payouts are delivered to executives and billions in dividends go to shareholders, while these monopoly businesses oversee deteriorating river standards and underinvestment. To me, a profits-driven industry that increases its takings as we use more water has the wrong incentives. Neither can it build the essential public trust for collaborative care and conservation. We know savings and efficiency come from metering, but even now only 50–60% of households are metered, and most private abstractions are unmetered. Water companies publish plans for resource management every five years. Affinity, which supplies water to most of Hertfordshire, is showing encouraging shifts to reduce abstraction and increase metering, but questions have to be asked about the level of ambition and enforceability.[10]

The Environment Agency in 2020 revealed that water quality is declining – none of the rivers within England and Wales reached a 'good' chemical quality and only 14% of rivers in England were in 'good' ecological condition. The issue came to prominence with a Parliamentary vote in October 2021 on the 'Duke of Wellington' amendment to restrict the dumping of raw sewage.[11] This was rejected then substituted by a much watered-down version by government, with a vague requirement and distant timetable to 'end the practice by 2050'. This lacks the required urgency, rather like the 2050 net zero timetable for climate action.

The European Court ruled in 2012 that the UK had breached a 1991 directive on releasing raw sewage, doing so not just 'in exceptional circumstances' as permitted.[12] We were assured Brexit wasn't supposed to undermine EU-wide environmental standards, such as the Water Framework Directive, but in August 2022, under the banner of removing 'EU red tape', the dumping of untreated sewage become generally permitted for the first time.[13]

A disclaimer: I'm a town planner and urban designer, not an ecologist or hydrologist. I walk a lot and that in itself is an education. I love the countryside. Who doesn't? I also follow the science on the climate and

....

10   Affinity Water, *Draft Water Resources Management Plan* 2024, November 2022. It aims to halve leaks by 2050 and increase metering to 75% by 2025.
      https://affinitywater.uk.engagementhq.com/wrmp.

11   The Rivers Trust, 'Parliamentary Briefing: Environment Bill. Lords Amendment 45B on Sewage Pollution', November 2021. https://theriverstrust.org/about-us/news/parliamentary-briefing-environment-bill-lords-amendment-45b-on-sewage-pollution.

12   BBC News, 'UK faces fine on EU water breach', 18 October 2012.
      https://www.bbc.co.uk/news/science-environment-19995081.

13   Feargal Sharkey statement on Twitter, 21 August 2022.
      https://twitter.com/Feargal_Sharkey/status/1561268615600562177?s=20.

ecological crises. My working background of three decades in planning applications and policy have given a core knowledge and insights into aspects of water drainage and the work of the Environment Agency and its predecessor the National Rivers Authority, as well as knowledge about development and access issues. I have studied hard to update myself on the vital questions of water. Yet for all the above, we are ultimately limited by personality view[14] and partial knowledge. So, this book is intended as a positive contribution to the debate. It's in collaborative discussion, listening to others and teamwork that we will make our best decisions. How do we make the necessary radical changes easier for people, and fair to all? No one likes to be told to change the way they live. Yet who isn't willing to make changes when they know it's the best way to guarantee clean and healthy rivers?

I hope this journey around Hertfordshire offers an enjoyable read, promotes a few good ideas and cultivates a greater priority for the natural world. As indigenous peoples such as the Māori understand, humans and water are intertwined. If we harm the river, we harm our own community. Our ancestors live on in the natural world and it is our duty to protect the land we inherit. 'I am the river and the river is me.'

We will all be the healthier for it.

---

14 'Personality view' or self-view, *Sakyaditthi* in Pali, is one of three key fetters to enlightenment in Buddhist teachings. The Thai forest teacher, Ajahn Chah expounds here. https://www.dhammatalks.net/Books/Ajahn_Chah_Clarity_of_Insight.pdf

'There is nothing simply nothing half so much
doing as simply messing about in boats' said the
Water Rat.

Foreword

"If we harm the river, we harm our own community"

Foreword by Peter Ruffles

My guess is that you may have a lasting friendship with one or other of those small pocket books or guides which in your earlier years informed, excited, stimulated, asserted. The Observer series did that for me, as did the News Chronicle's I-Spy books, and Ian Allan's little bibles for trainspotters, The Railway Locomotives' ABC!

With *Chalk Stream Reflections*, Tim Hagyard gives us something not dissimilar. He has provided a much-needed Hertfordshire volume, and filled a curiously unlikely gap on the local interest bookshelves. His style is so attractive and text so readable that one almost forgets that one is being informed and, yes, excited.

Chalk streams, rare in the world, are present in our county in considerable numbers. Tim describes our Hertfordshire 'streams' various characteristics, their current troubles and the values they bring today as in the past to the Hertfordshire landscape and people. Our special custodianship of Hertfordshire chalk streams brings a serious responsibility for our community; and there is urgency. For those we elect to advance our causes in councils and parliaments, there is an especial weight of responsibility.

It is important for me to say that solemn bit. Our times have introduced enormous and very serious challenges as Hertfordshire population has grown and although many of our industries have cleaned up and The

Lea through Hertford no longer carries 'iceberg mountains of foam' downstream on wash days in Luton, more abstractions and pollutions have been allowed. There is much more to be said about the threatening of chalk stream habitats, currently, and concerns must lead to responsible urgent action.

However, "Chalk Stream Reflections", is a volume intended to bring pleasure and joy. Tim's travels, researches, interpretations, are those of a scientific mind; a man fully aware of the nature of good town and country planning, and the need for homes; but a man who loves detail and beauty and quirks, and above all, for the benefit of us all, a man who loves Hertfordshire, our communities, climate, heritage and natural environment.

You will enjoy, appreciate and value this great addition to your bookshelf, and, on the excursions Tim suggests, your rambler's pocket.

Peter Ruffles MBE
(Honorary Alderman at Hertfordshire County Council)

Rivers of Hertfordshire

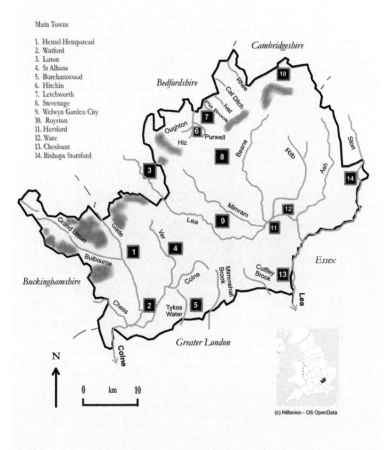

Main Towns

1. Hemel Hempstead
2. Watford
3. Luton
4. St Albans
5. Borehamwood
6. Hitchin
7. Letchworth
8. Stevenage
9. Welwyn Garden City
10. Royston
11. Hertford
12. Ware
13. Cheshunt
14. Bishops Stortford

Cambridgeshire

Bedfordshire

Buckinghamshire

Essex

Greater London

N

0   km   10

(c) Nilfanion - OS OpenData

'Do you know I've never before been in a boat'
said the Mole.

Western Hertfordshire

Main Towns

1. Hemel Hempstead
2. Watford
3. Luton
4. St Albans
5. Borehamwood
6. Hitchin
7. Letchworth
8. Stevenage
9. Welwyn Garden City
10. Royston
11. Hertford
12. Ware
13. Cheshunt
14. Bishops Stortford

Cambridgeshire

Bedfordshire

Essex

Buckinghamshire

Greater London

Rhee
Cat Ditch
Ivel
Pix Brook
Oughton
Hiz
Purwell
Beane
Rib
Ash
Stort
Mimram
Lea
Gade
Ver
Grand Union
Bulbourne
Chess
Colne
Tykes Water
Mimmshall Brook
Cuffley Brook

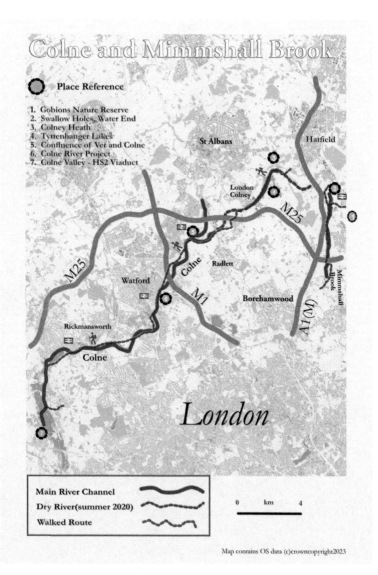

Route Map for Colne Mimshall Brook

1. The Colne and the Mimmshall Brook – dwindling and disappearing

The river Colne is the main river in western Hertfordshire, fed by several others. Passing the towns of Colney Heath, London Colney, Watford and Rickmansworth, it provides the longest route to the sea for any rain falling in Hertfordshire. In the two days I walked to explore the river I was disappointed to find areas of low flow, stagnation and dried-up riverbeds.

The westerly route of the Colne dates back 450,000 years to the events of the last ice age. An original 'proto-Thames' flowed from Wales across England and Hertfordshire to the North Sea but was gradually forced south by the Anglian Ice Sheet as it extended down from the north almost to present-day London. Meltwaters built up and broke through at Goring Gap to send the Thames south and elsewhere lay down sand and gravel deposits. A Lake Hertford appeared and the west section of this reversed south to become the present river Colne. The ice age certainly left its mark. If it hadn't happened then who knows, London might have ended up somewhere around Royston.

The Colne, not to be confused with the river Colne in Essex, possibly takes its meaning from Celtic words for 'stony river'. Walking from Roestock, I couldn't reach the river source within the private estate of North Mymms Park, former site of a sixteenth-century Jacobean house which overlooked the parkland and a once much grander river. The river in the park would make a good public path (map 1). My first meeting with the Colne was a poor sight. No meaningful river flow, even allowing for the fact that 2020 was a dry year. In a deep river channel, just a few patches of static water.

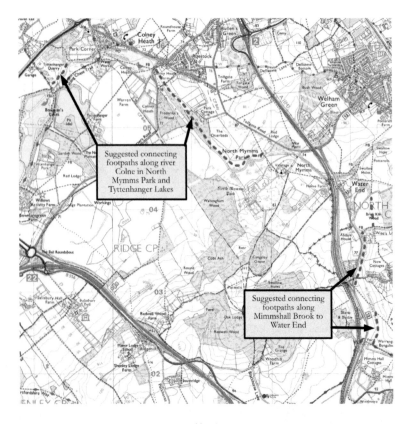

Map 1

Tracking the river's course, I crossed the common of Colney Heath, once grazed by livestock, long since ceased due to the hazards of road traffic. The path took me into former gravel workings at Tyttenhanger, now a popular angler's and picnic site with fishing lakes fed by the Colne. It's strange how the lakes of this old minerals site are on such a grand scale, yet the river that supplies them barely flows. It also shows how much water can be lost in a leak.

Heading south-west I passed Bowmans Farm, with a busy children's adventure theme park alongside the Colne (photo 1). The river gains a bit more size and widens as it reaches London Colney; the worn-out areas show that it's clearly a popular walk, but it felt neglected. Why not provide a surfaced path? The village was named as the main London road crosses the river Colne, and is marked by a listed eighteenth-century red-brick bridge, refashioned by the famous Victorian engineer Thomas Telford (photo 2). The bridge frames one side of the space along the river and the village green, but looked too big for the water beneath it. Only one of its seven arches had any water present and that was little more than a trickle. The river can still break its banks at times and there was localised flooding in the area in 2000.

1. Bowman's Farm.

2. London Colney Bridge.

Just west of London Colney are Broad Colney Lakes, more fishing waters created from older 1920s gravel working. West of Broad Colney the footpath came into a totally dried-up section of the riverbed – it simply disappeared. The whole river valley which lies close to the M25 felt quite barren, and the scale of earthworks at the Tarmac Lafarge asphalt plant and gravel workings, south of the M25, added to a sense of desolation. There was no water in the Colne as it passed below the Midland Mainline rail bridge. So, in July 2020, I found a 3km central section of one of Hertfordshire's main rivers to be dry.

West of Old Watling Street (A5183) the river recovered a little as it was joined by the Tykes Water, and the stream meandered down a quiet pleasant green valley forming intermittent pools of water and lined by willow trees. A low dam in the river looked simple and attractive but would obstruct aquatic life. A pumping station here marks the site of the Colne Water Company in Bushey, the first public water company, set up in 1873 to supply London. It was vigorously opposed by mill owners and anglers. As rail lines were built from the mid nineteenth century, so came urban development and 'Metroland', and a rapid increase in the population of south-west Herts. The 1892 Private Street Works Act ensured treatment of street and waste was charged to ratepayers, before that discharge of local sewers from housing areas was unregulated with some disastrous impacts on watercourses. The Colne became so polluted that anglers and landowners had to be compensated. The Colne Water Company combined with others in 1994 to create Three Valleys Water Company, which later became Veolia and is now all part of Affinity, the main water supplier for Hertfordshire.

In a quieter stretch I heard something move in the water. Was it a vole or an otter? The water was deep enough and seemed cleaner. Maybe I'd have seen something with more time or binoculars, but as I peered into the river all I could spot was a red and white plastic highways barrier. At this point the Colne 'captures' the larger Ver river coming down from St Albans (photo 3), grabbing its name as it flows on to Watford. The OS map describes the next section as the Ver-Colne – a compromise of sorts. Certainly, the valley here is expansive as if a much larger river flowed here, and the 'proto-Thames' did a very long time ago. I walked down the north side of the valley to a crossing over the M1 and reached the outskirts of Watford.

3. Colne captures the Ver.

The Colne is part of a valuable green finger flowing close to Watford town centre but separated from it by its busy ring road. 'Rediscovering the River Colne' is a ten-year project of Watford Council, Herts and Middlesex Wildlife Trust and others in the Colne Catchment Action Network, begun in 2020.[15] This is being funded to improve river access and water quality; the plan notes a perception of the river in Watford as dirty, inaccessible, unkempt and of low wildlife value. The project is all to the good, but it can't of itself address all the issues of river flow and water quality, nor remove the impact of traffic noise. It would be hoped the project includes measures to upgrade filters for road run-off. Encouragingly the project has identified and addressed a number of properties with misconnected drains that were sending foul sewer contents straight into the Colne, there are estimates that 1 in 5 properties may suffer misconnections.

15 *Rediscovering the River Colne*. https://www.rivercolnewatford.co.uk/. In the initial development phase it will create a habitat and access improvement strategy. https://www. westwatfordhistorygroup.org/2020/03/the-river-colne.html.

The riverside at Oxhey Park, South Watford was buzzing with young people attracted in good weather to a large skateboard park. I walked on along the old Ebury Railway Line, which provides excellent cycling between Watford and Rickmansworth and safe passage along the Colne Valley for several miles. At Rickmansworth, the river Colne merges with the river Chess and then weaves its way around lakes alongside the Grand Union Canal, its final Hertfordshire section. I followed the towpath, as a footpath along the Colne wasn't always provided. The towpath was narrow for the numbers needing to use it, so I had to pause at times to let others pass, but it works because the pace of life on the canal is slower and easier-going – a kinder, more forgiving world.

The Colne Valley Park stretches away to the south on the western fringe of Greater London. I climbed the slope to look across the lakes of the Colne Valley, where the route of HS2 will briefly cut into Hertfordshire before heading into a ten-mile tunnel beneath the Chilterns. In summer 2022 construction began on the Colne Valley Viaduct, at 2.1 miles (3.4km) the UK's longest railway bridge, crossing a series of lakes and waterways in the Colne Valley just outside London.

The Colne Valley Park Community Interest Company (CIC) was formed in 2012 to enhance the landscape, provide opportunities for recreation, foster a sustainable rural economy and encourage community participation. The park is already crossed by the M25 and the M40 and a new railway viaduct for HS2 will dramatically change the character of the valley. It will be interesting to see how well the company can meet all these challenges, not least the ongoing damage from motorway noise / air pollution and road run-off.

Back up at the Colne's headwaters and east of the A1(M) lies a short stream, the Mimmshall Brook, which flows north then disappears into a series of swallow holes in the chalk at Water End. In times of flood, water will follow a westerly channel and supplement the headwater of the Colne.

The Mimmshall Brook mostly feeds underwater streams that connect east to the Lea. It is something of an oddity. I had to follow paths across the private golf course of Dryden Park, Barnet to find any sign of its source close to where it rises outside Hertfordshire. The brook heads north under the M25, behind the South Mimms Service Station on the A1(M) where there is the quiet picnic area at Wash Lane Common. The path runs over a narrow eighteenth-century bridge. Strange to think horse drawn coaches once hurtled along here on the main road between London and Holyhead. The bridge remains but now it's a quiet walker's backwater.

Ecological records reveal that the Mimmshall Brook is performing as badly as any river in Hertfordshire.[16] One can speculate on the reasons, but I have to wonder whether it doesn't suffer for being so close and aligned with both the M25 and the A1(M), receiving large amounts of metals and other chemicals in road run-off. It's an issue campaigners know we are not taking seriously enough.[17]

Nearby Brookmans Park is Gobions Nature Reserve, an eighteenth-century landscape designed by Charles Bridgeman, now a public park centred on a large lake. Water runs off, feeding into the Mimmshall. I descended wooded paths along dried-up tributaries to meet the brook, which had a modest flow of water (only 0.18m deep according to monitoring). Using roads where new paths would help (map 1). I finally came to Water End, a designated Site of Special Scientific Interest and a distinctive habitat due to the presence of a group of fifteen sinkholes as streams drain over the London Clay close to the chalk outcrop. At times of flood a lake appears here but eventually drains back into the natural sinks. Subsurface dye tests have shown the water drains eventually

---

16 See Environment Agency, 2022 River Basin Management Plan maps. https://www.gov.uk/guidance/river-basin-management-plans-updated-2022.

17 See talk on road run-off by Jo Bradley of Stormwater Shepherds to Ver Society, 14 June 2022. https://www.riverver.co.uk/open-meeting-tues-14-june-road-runoff/.

through the chalk to the east and the river Lea.[18] The overflow channel to the west and the Colne may be a meltwater channel from the time of the Anglian glaciation. The channel takes water in flood from Water End under the A1(M) to the course of the Colne river. I didn't get to witness it myself but it sounds like a great wet-weather activity.

....

18 The dye experiments were undertaken in the 1920s and written up in the report by Morris, R.E. and Fowler, C.H. 1937 to the Metropolitan Water Board, London. https://www. northmymmshistory.uk/2018/07/the-natural-history-around-water-end.html

Grand Union Canal - Bulbourne

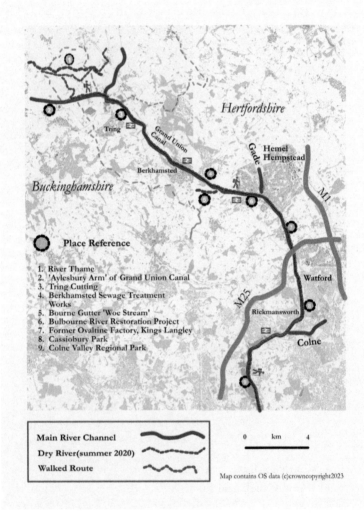

Place Reference

1. River Thame
2. 'Aylesbury Arm' of Grand Union Canal
3. Tring Cutting
4. Berkhamsted Sewage Treatment Works
5. Bourne Gutter 'Woe Stream'
6. Bulbourne River Restoration Project
7. Former Ovaltine Factory, Kings Langley
8. Cassiobury Park
9. Colne Valley Regional Park

Main River Channel

Dry River(summer 2020)

Walked Route

0   km   4

Map contains OS data (c)crowncopyright2023

Route Map for Grand Union / Bulbourne

2. The Grand Union Canal – drawing heavily on the Bulbourne

The Grand Union was not the first man-made waterway in Hertfordshire. The Lea in 1425 was the first river to be improved by Act of Parliament. The Grand Union though was certainly its most significant. Originally the Grand Junction Canal, by 1805 it linked London directly with the Oxford Canal, Birmingham and the Midlands. This transformed the movement of heavy goods, minerals and waste. It was the M40 or HS2 of its time and brought new industries, cheaper coal and other changes such as the wider distribution of London bricks and Welsh slates in construction.

For Hertfordshire it shifted development pressures west, when historically settlement and population had tilted to the east. The Grand Union runs north–south close to the western edge of the county, abstracting and capturing water that would otherwise flow into the Bulbourne, Gade and Colne.

My walk started from the station at Cheddington, Buckinghamshire, with a friend called Ingrid. We set out across the open plains north of the Chilterns Ridgeway in search of the river Thame; a search which proved to be in vain. The river Thame, confusingly a tributary of the Thames, is shown on the OS map briefly running from the north-west corner of Hertfordshire into Buckinghamshire. Not unexpectedly, on higher ground and in late September, we found no water in its channel.

We turned south until we reached the tranquil 'Aylesbury Arm' of the Grand Union Canal, near Puttenham (photo 4). It was a pleasant surprise. This area had a wilder, more rustic feel characterised by narrow single-boat locks and a verdant canal-side. Some thoughtfully designed new homes faced the canal at Wilstone, and I wondered how controversial that planning story had been (they often are.) The canal had provision for angling as well as for walkers; the branch offers a sleepy and safe six-mile footpath directly linking the Grand Union back to the centre of Aylesbury, Buckinghamshire, which lies to the west.

4. The Aylesbury Arm.

The canal is popular and easy walking. The first canal boats were pulled by horses, so bridges were designed to allow them to cross the path of the canal without pause. Eventually steam and diesel replaced the horses, so now the towpaths and the bridges are there for walkers, joggers and occasional cyclists.

At Marsworth, we reached the Tring group of reservoirs (1806–17) which thronged with Sunday visitors (photo 5). Narrowboats were selling drinks, ice creams and colourful craftwork. For the next three miles, the canal continued southwards into the deep and heavily wooded Tring Cutting that was dug into the chalk aquifer and the Chiltern Hills. The Canal was an amazing engineering feat, but the reservoirs, boreholes and pumping stations to support it made big demands on local rivers. The impacts of water abstraction were contested from the outset, especially by mill owners who struggled and often had to close their businesses as flows weakened. The river Bulbourne, a main feeder of the canal, used to begin 5km further north at a lake in Bulbourne. When I spotted it first at Berkhamsted it was a shallow stream in woodland, below the level of the canal. A footbridge over the canal and river links Berkhamsted town centre and a Waitrose store with areas on the east side.

5. Marsworth Reservoir.

In the late afternoon light, moorings enlivened the canal scene creating quite a theatre of narrowboats. Berkhamsted's riverside pubs were busy with weekend trippers and others; a real people presence. No wonder people enjoy living on the canal. As we walked beyond the town, the canal's attractions were lost as we encountered foul smells from Berkhamsted treatment works. This is on record as the worst offending site in the county for untreated overspills, as identified by the Hertfordshire CPRE[19] and the Rivers Trust website. A total of 168 overflow spills into the Grand Union Canal took place in 2021, for a cumulative 3,770 hours. The reason given by the Environment Agency was 'infiltration affecting performance'. Hmm. Hardly an adequate explanation.

South of the Bulbourne a short three-mile tributary, the Bourne Gutter, feeds into the main Bulbourne. As a winterbourne it only flows in wetter years from springs near Hockeridge Bottom. Local legend considered it a 'Woe Stream' – its flow every 4–5 years would be a sign of pending disaster.

At Winkwell, the Three Horseshoes pub is perfectly placed by a swing bridge road crossing of the Grand Union, with lines of canal-side seating and tables. The river Bulbourne came more fully into view and looked a lot heathier as we progressed into the commons at Hemel Hempstead. Here are river meadows that lie between the town centre and its railway station. A board announced the award-winning *Bulbourne River restoration project* completed between 2013 to 2017 (photo 6).[20]

....
19   CPRE Hertfordshire, 'Latest raw sewage figures'. https://www.cpreherts.org.uk/news/latest-raw-sewage-figures-whats-in-hertfordshires-waterways/.
20   The Box Moor Trust, 'Bringing back the Bulbourne – our award-winning success story'. https://www.boxmoortrust.org.uk/river-bulbourne/.

6. Bulbourne restoration.

The river had been greatly compromised by the Grand Union Canal and was listed under the Natural Environment and Communities Act 2006 as a priority for restoration. The subsequent work – regrading of shallower banks, creation of new wetland habitats, reed beds etc. – was led by the Box Moor Trust. This rewilding of the river has restored its former meandering character with immediate benefits for biodiversity, and it's all enjoyed in a central public space. It was beyond the scope of the project to address all the issues of water supply and pollution, but it was really encouraging to see the benefits physical restoration can bring.[21]

The Bulbourne is then captured by the Gade which accompanies the Grand Union Canal south of Hemel Hempstead, where only a few sections of the natural river course remain. The Grand Union was a commercial venture that grew quickly as a business corridor. I passed the former paper-milling site at Apsley in Hemel Hempstead and the

21   See 'Principles of Chalk Stream Restoration – Catchment Based Approach', *Implementation Plan* 2021. https://catchmentbasedapproach.org/learn/chalk-stream-strategy-3/.

Ovaltine factory in Kings Langley, which once had its own fleet of seven narrowboats. The industries are gone now but both buildings have been attractively converted for housing. The roar of M25 traffic announced itself long before the motorway bridge passed overhead. Beyond this, the canal entered a tree-lined section; one of its bends was straightened in the past after a coal-laden boat sank. I crossed the canal at a distinctive listed roving bridge, the one-horse wide Lady Capel Bridge (photo 7). The Lady Capel Wharf was a delivery point for London coal, close to the coal tax boundary that once ringed the city.

7. Lady Capel Bridge.

Cassiobury Park serves Watford well and has been voted one of the top parks in the country, inheriting the landscaped estate of French-inspired avenues that were once the grounds to the country house of the 5th Earl of Essex. The earl demanded the new canal be landscaped as it passed his land, and located on the far side of the river away from his house. The country house was later demolished in the 1920s, to be replaced by a new housing estate as Watford expanded.

After Cassiobury the canal straightened as it headed south-west out of Watford. South of the canal is common land at Croxley – now a site of botanical interest, it has recovered from the disturbance of gravel extraction here and at Rickmansworth when back in the 1920s minerals were extracted to build the first Wembley stadium. The river Gade merges into the river Colne west of Watford, and the Colne then follows the Grand Union Canal to London. The Batchworth junction on the canal at Rickmansworth was well located for mills and industry, including boat building. A 1980s Tesco supermarket has replaced the Walker Brothers boatbuilders on Frogmore Wharf, but frankly it has not aged well. Its lifeless brick walls offer no meaningful design references, nor is there any riverside space alongside the canal for other activity. In this final section of the Grand Union in Hertfordshire I passed increasingly large numbers of narrowboats closer to London, a pattern similar to that seen as I walked down the river Lea in eastern Hertfordshire.

I moved away for 'buffering distance' from Thames Water's Maple Lodge Sewage Treatment Works. The wind was in an unfavourable direction. You wonder how tolerable this facility is for people living nearby. This giant treatment plant opened in 1950 with a site at Blackbirds Farm in Aldenham to serve the whole of West Hertfordshire. In post war years the Colne Valley saw the dumping of old narrowboats[22] by the British Transport Commission and others before people realised that there was a market for their conversion. British Waterways, formed in 1962, was part of that transition story. The canals moved from decline and a lost industrial role into a successful era of leisure use. The network now sees more boating on the canals than was ever seen due to industry. British Waterways was replaced by the Canal and Rivers Trust in 2012.

The final stop on the Grand Union Canal in Hertfordshire was Black Jack's lock, with its seventeenth-century cottage and former mill.

....
22   Canal and River Trust. Herbert Dunkley Collection, *Abandoned narrowboats at Harefield Flash on the Grand Union Canal* https://collections.canalrivertrust.org.uk/bw197.2.27.22

Reputedly a slave, bought and sold with the land, he was hired to enforce payments from boats who passed through the lock but did it so successfully that he was murdered. His ghost is said to haunt the lock. The full verified story of his life and its tragic end is sadly not available.

With pressure mounting on supplies in a water-stressed region, and the need to reduce abstraction from the chalk aquifer, the use of the Grand Union for strategic transfer of water was proposed in November 2022 by Affinity Water in its Draft Water Resources Management Plan 2024[23]. This would see the canal used to bring 50 million litres a day of water down from the Midlands to the South East, an interesting additional new role for the canal network which has the support of the Canal Rivers Trust and other stakeholders. So, the canal takes on the role of water conduit and is expanded beyond leisure. At a cost of £250m investment, is it good value and what of the energy costs of water transfer? Quite what it means for water quality, leisure and ecological interests it's not for me to say – but hopefully, as indicated in the plan, it may support further reduction of abstraction from the chalk aquifers.

---

23   Affinity Water, *Draft Water Resources Management Plan* 2024, November 2022. https://affinitywater.uk.engagementhq.com/wrmp.

River Ver

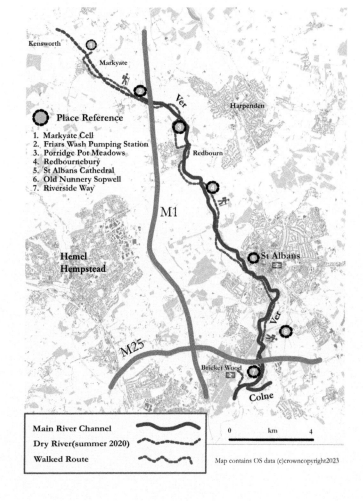

Kensworth

Markyate

Ver

Harpenden

Place Reference

1. Markyate Cell
2. Friars Wash Pumping Station
3. Porridge Pot Meadows
4. Redbournebury
5. St Albans Cathedral
6. Old Nunnery Sopwell
7. Riverside Way

Redbourn

M1

Hemel
Hempstead

St Albans

Ver

M25

Bricket Wood

Colne

Main River Channel	
Dry River(summer 2020)	
Walked Route	

0   km   4

Map contains OS data (c)crowncopyright2023

Route Map for Ver

3. The Ver –
where history flows strong

The river Ver ... The river Ver! I repeated it to myself as I walked. A play on words and bit of a tongue twister. I decided to stick with *The Ver*. The Ordnance Survey map marks the source of the Ver, north of Hertfordshire in Kensworth, Bedfordshire, in the Chilterns Area of Outstanding Natural Beauty. From here it follows the old A5 (A5183), the Roman Watling Street which linked London and Anglesey.

I decided to avoid the main road so went first to Church End at the north end of Markyate. Here I duly found a dried-up river channel and my first 'River Ver Trail' blue metal badge on the bridge parapet, courtesy of the Ver Valley Society. The Society together with Herts County Council have delivered a 17-mile walk the length of the river with waymarking signs and several oak benches, artistically etched with river scenes and a trail map. I tried several of them out as I went on my way.

The Ver runs close to the A5, parallel to what is now the long high street of Markyate. The river follows the valley down to the A5 junction with the M1. The outfall of the Markyate Sewage Treatment Works (Thames Water) seemed to provide the main water flow for the river here. In 2021, data records indicated sewer storm overflows spilled 139 times for a total of 2,642 hours, discharging into the river Ver.[24] Many dry-weather spills in late 2021 took place too and explanations are needed.

Near to Flamstead, by the M1 junction, was the sorry picture of the old Chequers Inn, a listed building, last a pub in the 1950s. It's been unoccupied over ten years and looks vulnerable. It lies on the overgrown channel of the river Ver at Friars Wash, a spot that historically was often in flood. The building's heritage value seemed lost amidst fast-moving

....
24 The Rivers Trust, *Raw Sewage in our Rivers*. https://theriverstrust.org/key-issues/sewage-in-rivers.

traffic racing down to the M1. What I would give to see it restored, with a pub garden on a new walker's path along the Ver, with replenished river flow and wildlife. (See path suggestion – map 2).

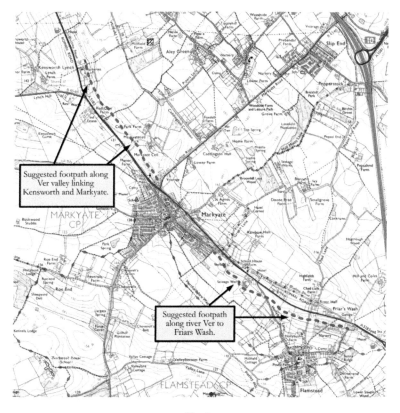

Map 2

Evidence reveals human habitation beside the Ver for thousands of years. The valley is dotted with the names and stories of religious sites, such as the twelfth-century Pilgrim Roger who, after a visitation of angels on return from Jerusalem, took up a hermit cell at Markyate. The Ver at that time was big enough to float funeral boats downstream to St Albans. People played and fished in the river as recently as the 1920s.

The National Rivers Authority (forerunner of the Environment Agency) once revealed that 70% of the river Ver flow was taken up for public water supply. UK TAG guidelines say it should be only 5–10%. Over-abstraction has long been recognised as a problem for all chalk streams going back to the 1950s.[25] Affinity Water[26] are licensed to extract 30 million litres a day from the Ver by the Environment Agency, far more than is desirable, but it's better than the 1980s when it was 60–65 million litres a day. The Friars Wash pumping station, opened in 1956 near Flamstead, dramatically reduced flows by 15 million litres a day but after campaigning by the Ver Valley Society this was reduced to a limit of 1 million litres a day and standby status in 1993. Its full closure is now promised.

Crossing hostile roundabouts and the M1 Junction 9, it was good to move into open country and the gentle inclines of the Upper Ver Valley. At first, I struggled to pick up the river and the designated footpath. On reaching a dwelling at Verlam End, the stream was in definite flow. From here the path went south, albeit at a distance from the river. By the time I reached the Redbourn Golf Club it had become a more substantial body of water. Beside a footbridge crossing I noted a long, sickly green-brown covering of sludge that extended some thirty metres. It was as bad as anything I saw during the summer of 2020 (photo 8). Was it the failure of a private cesspit, a misconnected drain, a sewage spill from works or a farm?

....

25   A 1951 report of Hertfordshire County Council noted abstraction was the cause of diminishing water levels to the London Basin.

26   The three separate Veolia Water-branded businesses, Veolia Water Central, Veolia Water Southeast and Veolia Water East, were brought together as one company under the Affinity Water brand in 2012.

8. River pollution.

The Ver Trail led me through the fields of Rothamsted, the world's oldest agricultural research facility. Porridge Pot Meadows is one of the best areas to enjoy the river, with scope to restore it as accessible wetland for the enjoyment of the village (map 3). Over seventy years, the perennial head of the river has moved 5km downstream from Markyate to Redbourn.[27] Hopefully that will move back if abstraction rates fall. I crossed the river to pick up the Nickey Line, a former railway that linked Harpenden with Hemel Hempstead until the 1950s. A local survey was pinned up reporting 12,000 walking and cycling trips a week on the Nickey Line during the lockdown. It's well used! Leaving the village, the Ver waters are bolstered by flow from the river Red tributary which receives the murky and potentially toxic water run-off from the M1.

27 Chilterns Chalk Stream Project, *Celebrating 25 Years Report* 2022. https://www.chilternstreams.org/our-work/25-years-of-the-chilterns-chalk-streams-project/.

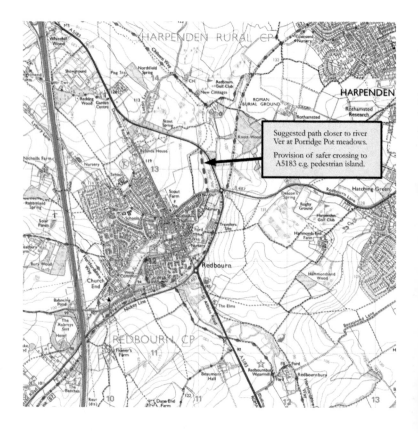

Within the map:

HARPENDEN RURAL CP

HARPENDEN

Suggested path closer to river
Ver at Porridge Pot meadows.

Provision of safer crossing to
A5183 e.g. pedestrian island.

Redbourn

REDBOURN CP

Map 3

Further south at Redbournebury, the Ver is graced by the presence of
its last working watermill, which still produces its own organic flour
and bakes bread sold on-site. I was sorely tempted to join the queue for
its sourdough and wholemeal loaves. We rightly enjoy these remaining
mills – the Ver once had a dozen – but it's worth remembering that in
their day they made their own demands on the rivers. In social terms
protectionist milling rights prevented poor peasants from grinding their

own flour. Hand mills would be seized and destroyed, even in people's own homes, to protect the market of the mill owners. It was one of the issues that led to the Peasants' Revolt of 1381.

The river looked healthy here. A solitary cow had escaped the herd and bent down blissfully munching her way through dense patches of watercress (photo 9), a plant that has long thrived in the clear waters of Hertfordshire's chalk streams. These meadows are good bird-spotting terrain with rare reports of cattle egrets and hen harriers. Water vole were reintroduced in autumn 2021 and reports suggest they are increasing their territorial area. A farm road fords the river here and the path on the eastern side of the river leads down to another old mill at Shafford. A painted sign on the mill cautioned '*Bathing and fishing prohibited*'.

9. Watercress feast.

The tower of St Albans Cathedral, as seen from the Crown Estate of Gorhambury, is surely one of the finest valley approaches into a Hertfordshire town. In the past it would have been a sight to lift the spirits of any pilgrims walking this way. Around 2,000 years ago, the Ver was a substantial water course amidst marshland, and an obstacle to travel. That it was a navigable river for boats and a crossing point for Watling Street was reason enough to establish the Roman town of Verulamium. It was the first British martyrdom, of Alban who had protected a local Christian priest, that brought pilgrimage and prominence to the site and eventually the new town, St Albans. Bede records that around AD 300, Alban walked up to his execution spot on the hill opposite Verulamium, and it was said that the waters of the Ver dried up so that he could proceed without delay. Within a 1980s housing estate is a brick-built well head in a small green, arguably the first Christian holy well in the country; legend has it that as Alban gasped for water heading for execution, a spring miraculously appeared at this point. There are other legends around Alban's execution, including that the first executioner paid with his life when he refused to carry out the task and that the eyes of the second popped out as he struck the fatal blow.

The abbey and town were established around the location of Alban's execution. It grew to be one of the main towns of Hertfordshire by the turn of the eighteenth century. In the seventeenth century, St Michael's Bridge was built as its first toll bridge over the Ver, although it is no longer the main route into town. When I passed, the Waffle House café, next to the bridge, was doing a brisk outdoor socially distanced trade. I entered the town park, historically an area of grazing land with fishponds that supplied the abbey; peasants were barred from fishing in the river or ponds. The park was reconstructed after World War I by ex-servicemen and proved a great asset for the town, now busy with people enjoying the summer, exploring its Roman remains and the lakes fed by the waters of the Ver. The river is easily followed through the park. A fading information sign tells the story of Hertfordshire's rare chalk streams and reminds us to use water wisely to help restore them. It was the drought of 1976, when the Ver dried up at St Albans, that prompted the formation of the now thriving Ver Valley Society.[28]

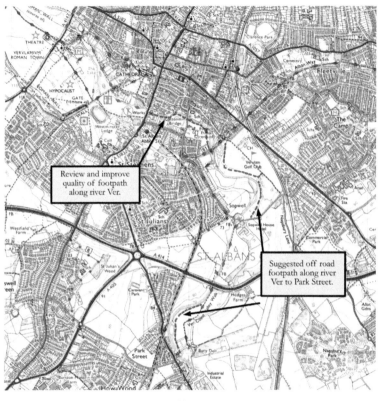

Map 4

South of St Albans, the Ver passes wildflower meadows at Sopwell, noted for their butterflies in spring. Near here was the site of an old nunnery, where Anne Boleyn may once have stayed. A river path through the

....
28 The excellent Ver Valley website (https://www.riverver.co.uk/) provides much information on the river. The society formed to protect the river has been challenging abstraction and water quality issues since 1976.

Verulum golf course nearer to the river would be a great improvement (map 4) The river after new Barnes Mill reassuringly looked much cleaner: the classic mirror-like calm of a chalk stream with *Ranunculus aquatilis* its trailing crowfoot water plants. Sopwell was in 1795 the planned terminal basin for a new canal to link to the Grand Union, but this was resisted by local landowners and abandoned. The Ver Trail goes under the A414 and on to Park Street, an area of watercress farming which was able to reach the markets of London via the Abbey branch line. It still runs up to St Albans. Nearby is the permitted site for a new rail freight depot which is now the subject of rival plans for housing. I passed the Red Lion pub in Frogmore where just a few decades ago tug-of-war events used to be held across the ford, the losing side being pulled into the river. There were summer regattas with parades of boats, people singing into the night as they floated by with lanterns.[29] What a sight that must have been. Times inevitably change, but much life as well as water has been lost from our rivers over the years.

After Frogmore I entered a network of clearly marked paths by lakes that have created encouraging new wetland habitat from former gravel pits. A bridge then takes you over the M25 and well away from the river. Outfalls from the motorway here will most likely be a problem. The run-off of chemicals, metals and plastics within tyre sediment from roads into the river is a widespread issue of river pollution but almost completely ignored by government and regulators.

The final walk along the Ver was Riverside Way, a near-mile-long public path alongside a fast-flowing stream, with seating to enjoy it and a handy public car park for family outings. The river here was straightened as 1970s gravel works were completed and the path created by Herts County Council as a countryside project with volunteers. A more holistic approach these days would most likely deliver a meandering

....
29   See book by Jacqui Banfield Taylor. *The River Ver A Meander Through Time* . Halsgrove. 2012

restoration. Just beyond this the Ver merges into, or is 'usurped' by, the river Colne, as it flows down to Watford and the Thames (photo 3).

While a few potential improvements did occur to me (maps 2-4), the Ver Valley Trail works well. Ten-year-old signs are being replaced. The Ver Society, with record membership, is clearly making a difference. Five decades after its founding, aquifer readings show improved groundwater levels and that abstraction is being cut back. The Bow Bridge Pumping Station, north of St Albans, closed in 2016. Nonetheless, the Environment Agency's Environmental Flow Indicator (EFI) still estimates that the Ver has a deficit of 24 million litres a day. In the summer drought of 2022, the river dried up beyond Redbournebury, and it disappeared in St Albans as recently as 2019. Affinity Water's plan set inappropriately low trigger points for hosepipe bans and they seem reluctant to activate drought orders, notwithstanding local protests about the harm being done to river ecology. Volunteers monitor for phosphates and nitrates in the water at ten separate spots every quarter. Clearance of non-native species such as Himalayan balsam regularly takes place. The river is steeped in history and the issue of its care galvanises the community. Its future feels more secure and all the better for its local champions at the Ver Valley Society.[30]

....
30 Under Affinity Water's Drought Management Plan, groundwater has to have fallen to Trigger Zone 3 before a hosepipe ban might be called – but in the Ver's case virtually all of the river would be gone by then. Ver Valley Society, 'Drought but no hosepipe ban!', 12 August 2022. https://www.riverver.co.uk/drought-but-no-hosepipe-ban/.

River Gade

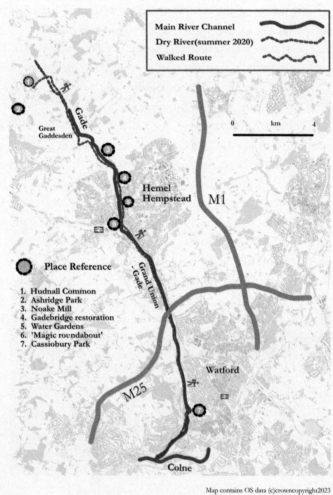

Main River Channel

Dry River(summer 2020)

Walked Route

Gade

Great
Gaddesden

0   km   4

Hemel
Hempstead

M1

Grand Union
- Gade

Place Reference

1. Hudnall Common
2. Ashridge Park
3. Noake Mill
4. Gadebridge restoration
5. Water Gardens
6. 'Magic roundabout'
7. Cassiobury Park

M25

Watford

Colne

Map contains OS data (c)crowncopyright2023

Route Map for Gade

4. The Gade – depleted but promising connections

The Gade is a relatively short (25km) chalk stream tributary of the river Colne. Its source is near to Dagnall in Buckinghamshire, but the perennial head is a long way south down the chalk valley, even when groundwater levels are healthier after a wet winter. Dagnall lies just outside Hertfordshire and a small sewage works sits in the valley, its treated water probably providing the only regular water outflow for the stream.

It was an early start from Hertford for the day's walking, beginning with a wooded descent from Hudnall Common. I wandered down into the gentle valley of the Gade, a landscape of the long dip slope of the Chiltern Downs and all part of the 47-mile-long chalk escarpment connected by the Icknield Way, 'Britain's Oldest Road', now the Ridgeway Path.[31]

I met with an early hazard due to the lack of a safe footpath. We have a fantastic inheritance of rights of way in England and Wales which we do slightly take for granted. Notwithstanding the dedication of local volunteers, officers and groups like the Ramblers, there are occasional serious gaps and scope for expansion. Government, and the Treasury especially, doesn't sufficiently value walking as transport. Significant long-term funds aren't allocated; budgets have a historic road-building bias. It can depend on which part of the country you are in and how well the rights of way service is funded. Hertfordshire does comparatively well, at least for waymarking, maintenance and enforcement, but there's always more work to be done.

So, when I reached Hudnall Corner on the fast and narrow B440 Dagnall Road I could find no safe route to go south. The road follows the Gade Valley but with high hedges tight to the roadside, blind bends

....
31   National Trails UK, 'The Ridgeway'. https://www.nationaltrail.co.uk/en_GB/trails/the-ridgeway/.

and no verge spaces either side of Dagnall Road – it didn't seem sensible to proceed. It would only take one speeding or inattentive moment by a driver. Logically, there should be a separate footpath and cycleway up the valley to connect the Icknield Way / Ridgeway in the north with Hemel Hempstead to the south. So, I took the life-preserving decision to trespass onto the adjacent field at Hudnall Corner. I managed to rip the seat of my trousers in the process, as I slightly misjudged ground levels while negotiating a low barbed-wire fence. It could have been worse. Later, on hearing a motorbike hurtling down the Dagnall Road, I felt vindicated in my decision.

Under the rules of the King's highway, other than trunk roads, all more vulnerable users – pedestrians, cyclists, horse riders, joggers, electric scooters etc. – have the right to be on the road. This does not mean that road speed limits or road designs are adjusted to protect them against the dangers of vehicles. Too often people in cars are distracted and make no allowance for the possible presence of others.

A new path down the Gade Valley, linking the Ridgeway with Hemel Hempstead to the south, would be a welcome addition (map 5) as part of a 'Gade Valley Path'. The valley and the river has potentially a more natural form north of Hemel Hempstead, whereas further downstream it was often widened for navigation. I eventually reached a public footpath (FP68) at the meadows below Great Gaddesden; it felt reassuringly familiar, like coming home, being close to my 'spiritual home' at the Amaravati Buddhist Monastery which lies on the ridge nearby. The paths from here follow the valley floor and there was a reasonable flow of water within the Gade. The river wandered a little and the stream once supported watercress beds. At Water End, the Gade opens into a sizeable lake and there is a view to be enjoyed from the narrow B440 road bridge as it crosses. The presence of these large bodies of water, attractive as they are, may give a false impression of the overall health and quantity of water in the river.

Map 5

Gaddesden Place stands high on the east side, a prominent local landmark, enjoying wide views across the Gade Valley. A large country manor house, built in 1774 for Thomas Helsey, the MP for Hertfordshire, it has served as a location for film and TV, most recently used in *Munich – The Edge of War*.

I passed Noake Mill, a substantial old mill building, now converted to residential. There's a modern replacement bridge over the mill race and the sluice gate needs redesigning to permit the passage of fish. The unofficial 'Gade Valley Path' continues around the back of a large fish farm, L. Cura and Sons. This was one of the first places to commercially farm goldfish. At Piccotts End Mill, where the pond and the mill race were dry, the Mill House is retained although the mill itself is a rebuild and the character of the setting heavily compromised by new housing. I arrived on the edge of Hemel Hempstead and paused to enjoy a small 'beach' in the Gadebridge area – part of Affinity Water's 'Revitalising Chalk Rivers' partnership with the Environment Agency and Dacorum Council. This work seemed to do in microcosm many things that one would like to see carried out on a much wider scale. It has created new wetlands to trap and improve the quality of run-off water into the river, and features to hold up the flow of water and diversify habitats. These are the kind of soft changes parts of the country have achieved by reintroducing wild beavers, a move that polls suggest has public support.[32]

The Gade flows down into the main town park as originally intended, connecting the town and the river as a centrepiece of the new town of Hemel Hempstead. This 'city in a park' was master-planned by the landscape architect Geoffrey Jellicoe. Information boards tell the story of the listed *Water Gardens* (photo 10). The casual eye wouldn't have guessed it, but the water design was modelled on a serpent. It adds to the story. I doubt Geoffrey Jellicoe would be so pleased by the presence of the large car park block which impinges the gardens to one side, but he would have appreciated the award-winning restoration of the Flower Garden in 2016. Overall, I couldn't help feeling the water gardens, like the River Gade itself, deserved to be much more centre stage within the town, accessible and restored as a restful natural sanctuary. Unwittingly it has been compromised by roads, car parking, the noise of traffic and

32 RSPB Partnership, *Troubled Waters Report,* September 2021. https://www.rspb.org.uk/globalassets/downloads/our-work/troubled-waters-report.

that dash for post-war 'growth'. At the bottom end of the town centre, the Gade has been restored as the central landscape feature of the new Riverside Shopping Centre, albeit slightly squeezed (photo 11). Just south of here the river passes beneath the A414 under the remarkably resilient 'magic roundabout'. When I first drove up to it, I recall it being a bewildering traffic junction. It gets easier to negotiate if you think of it as a tight sequence of six mini roundabouts. It has its fans, but I believe it stresses newcomers and regular users. If you try to follow the river, you experience the 'roundabout' as a hostile place. I darted across to the central green to see the Gade running calmly down the middle, oblivious to the swirl of traffic around. I think green space and paths to this area would add value (map 6). As urban designers might say, reprioritise it for people friendliness. If we can let go of this motordom oddity, it has great place-making potential.

10. Jellicoe's Water Gardens.

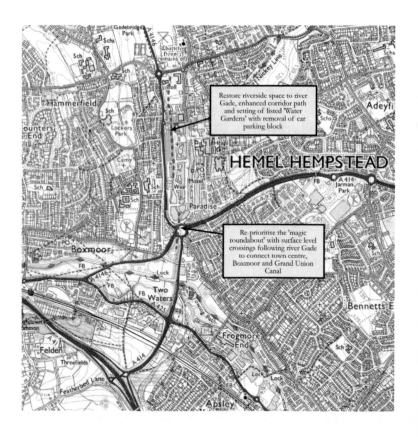

Map 6

11. Riverside Centre.

Two Waters was once a distinct village at the confluence of the Bulbourne and the Gade. A footpath through the Two Waters Park by the Gade leads down to its junction with the Grand Union Canal in the south of Hemel Hempstead. From here the river accompanies and is sometimes lost entirely to the canal. Only a few sections of the natural river course remain, such as a section under the M25 and another more substantial where it becomes a focal attraction for the public at Cassiobury Park, Watford.

The Gade is more natural, wider and more easily accessible at Cassiobury Park in Watford, following a winding course close to footpaths. The river was being enjoyed by a number of dogs off the lead, and it looks well suited for paddling and play. Perhaps this would be a good location for a designated public bathing site? Wild swimming and river bathing has taken off in recent years, notwithstanding reports of people falling ill due to water pollution. Rivers clean enough to swim in would be a good benchmark for water cleanliness. Designated river bathing sites remain scarce; the first was granted on the River Wharfe at Ilkley in December

2020. Such sites could support higher standards, as they require regular monitoring of water conditions. The more the merrier then.

Beyond Cassiobury the Gade passes into Croxley Common Moor west of Watford, and finally merges into the river Colne. To get back to the car at Hudnall I took a train from Watford to Berkhamsted, then walked across the National Trust-owned Ashridge estate. It's a privilege to have wide access across this landscape of beech woodlands and green fields, part-designed by Capability Brown who created 'The Golden Valley'. It was a long way round to end a long day. The last ten miles went slowly due to some knee pain, but I was able to walk it off. I had at least walked the length of the Gade, a stream significantly impacted by human activity and low groundwater levels. With wider restoration and improved green pathways, a Gade Valley Path would be a great way to link the Chilterns and the Ridgeway with Hemel Hempstead and the Grand Union.

River Chess

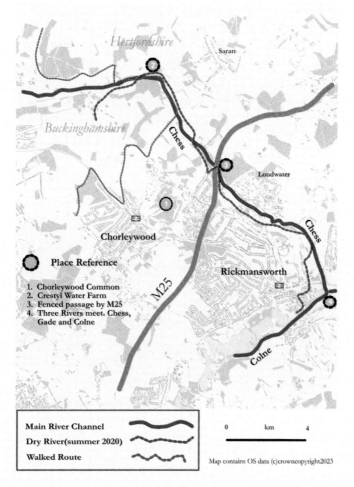

Place Reference

1. Chorleywood Common
2. Crestyl Water Farm
3. Fenced passage by M25
4. Three Rivers meet. Chess, Gade and Colne

Main River Channel	
Dry River(summer 2020)	
Walked Route	

0　　　km　　　4

Map contains OS data (c)crowncopyright2023

Route Map for Chess

5. The Chess –
a jewel in the Chilterns crown

The Chess is only about ten miles long, one of the shorter chalk streams in Hertfordshire. What it lacks in distance it certainly makes up for in quality. As I kept within Hertfordshire, I missed some of the delights of the Buckinghamshire section, Latimer Meadows and the upper Chess Valley.[33] Chesham is the source of the river just above the town. Apart from in drier years, the stream flows quietly along the backways of the town and through a local park, all the healthier for being upstream of the faltering Chesham Sewage Works.[34] It is estimated that between 40% and 80% of the Chess flow is treated effluent from this works. Unfortunately, even treated wastewater still contains damaging levels of nutrients such as phosphorus.

I began my roundabout walk of 30km from Chorleywood not far from the Chess. This village is centred on one of the great surviving commons of Hertfordshire, a 200-acre nature reserve. From there I walked up to the village of Chenies and then cut down steep valley sides to reach the river. As I crossed the footbridge by Crestyl Cottage, at one of the county's last watercress farms, the fast-flowing waters really struck home. As healthy as any chalk stream I'd seen (photo 12). The sunshine enhanced a lively bubbling clarity, and a fish, possibly a brown trout, leaped and splashed downstream. Trout are a good indicator species for river cleanliness. A letter on the noticeboard for Crestyl Water Farm explained that their fourth-generation cress beds had been devastated by pollution from Thames Water. Apparently, many sewage spills from Chesham Works had occurred between February and April 2020,

---

33 Latimer Meadows adorns the front cover of the literature celebrating the twenty-fifth anniversary of the Chilterns Chalk Streams Project: https://chalkstreams.org/25-years-of-the-chilterns-chalk-stream-project/.

34 In 2021, its sewer storm spilled into the Chess 116 times for a total of 1,814 hours, twice as often as in 2020.

exacerbating a shortage of water. The farm could pump its own water at great expense but it made the business unviable.

12. Crestyl Water Farm.

The Chess is known for a good range of wildlife, including brown trout and grayling. It retains one of the last remaining populations of water vole in the Chilterns, which nationally have declined drastically (97%) since the 1970s. Watercress farming thrived from the mid eighteenth century on the Ver, Chess and other rivers in the county, benefiting from the purity and constant temperature of chalk stream waters and the proximity to London markets. However, for various reasons, including water quality and foreign competition, the industry has been in steady decline. It remains to be seen whether the days of 'Cress from the Chess' will ever return, but it would be a good sign if it did.

A volunteer group, the River Chess Association,[35] are actively working and campaigning to enhance the river. Their Facebook page records

35   For more information see http://www.riverchessassociation.co.uk/.

beautiful images of Chess wildlife as well as shocking instances of the effects of sewage discharges. Many posts are concerned at government laxity and poor enforcement. The Association is fully engaged. It's signed up to a ten-year catchment plan (2021),[36] part of a 'smarter water catchments' initiative being piloted on the Chess.

Public footpaths on both sides of the Chess Valley led on to Sarratt Mill. The Chess Valley Walk is a well-marked route along paths and narrow lanes, a rural almost traffic-free idyll with groups of small cottages such as at Sarratt Bottom. I spotted a grass meadow marked as a 'friends retreat', providing a shared green area for local families that runs down to the river. Walking gets less comfortable as you reach the M25, which is intrusive and a barrier to movement down the valley. I used a road bridge to get over the motorway, but the next 500m south along the Chess Valley Walk was down a claustrophobic fenced passage just a few feet from the fumes and noise of motorway lorries. This right of way was presumably 'safeguarded' when the road was planned. On a map it may have looked adequate but in practice, it now offers an uninviting route which I suspect many would not wish to repeat (See photo 13). Traffic forecasts in 1986 were wildly below the eventual traffic levels on the M25, about three times beyond anticipated. A better alternative is needed here (map 7) – either a path on the east side of the Chess away from the M25 or, if something can be negotiated with the Tropical Marine Centre, along the west bank of the river.

....
36   Chess Smarter Water Catchment, https://chesssmarterwatercatchment.org/.

13. Fenced path by M25.

On the edge of Rickmansworth, the Chess Valley Walk moves away from the river as it threads its way between back garden fences. Not the most welcoming of routes. It included my first sighting of plastic fencing, another source of the microplastics getting into the environment, including our rivers. The village of Loudwater on the opposite side of the Chess alludes to a larger river Chess in the past. That said, by nature, chalk streams are never truly 'loud' but at most gentle playful streams flowing across steady declines. Most of the falls are man-made, at weirs for instance, and create barriers to aquatic life. South of Loudwater there are paths on either side of the river which could be better connected (map 7). The walk curves around the estate of the Royal Masonic School although the buildings are out of sight.

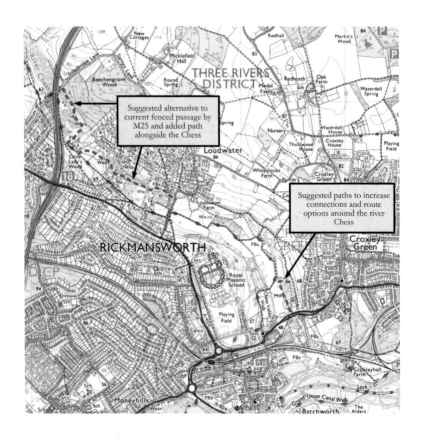

Map 7

I went into Rickmansworth town centre while trying to stay close to the river. A rather mean riverside path was being laid out alongside the Chess as it ran around a new Premier Inn. The path then joins the river Colne and the Grand Union Canal at Batchworth Lock. The confluence of the Chess, Gade and Colne at Rickmansworth give their name to the local district council 'Three Rivers'. The Chess, Gade and the Ver are part of the Chilterns Stream Project area which extends into Buckinghamshire, a partnership of nine voluntary and statutory bodies.[37]

There is some progress. Two pumping stations in the Chess Valley were closed in 2020 by Affinity Water. The final closure of Thames Water abstraction at Hawridge is intended for the current plan period (2025–30), as well as expansion of the critical Chesham Treatment Works. Affinity's most recent *Water Resources Management Plan* says they will reduce abstraction by 36 million litres a day in the upper Colne tributaries, which includes the Chess.

With this catchment plan for reduced abstraction, hopefully improvements to reduce phosphate discharges from Chesham SWT Works,[38] the training of forty citizen scientists to monitor the river conditions, and continuing local activism, the jewel in the heart of the Chilterns that is the Chess river has many 'guardian angels' and promises a healthier future.

---

37   The Chilterns Chalk Streams Project partners are Chilterns Conservation Board, Affinity Water, Buckinghamshire County Council, Chiltern District Council, Chiltern Society, the Environment Agency, Thames Water and the Wildlife Trust. https://www.chilternstreams.org/discover/.

38   River Chess Association, 'Sewage updates', March 2021. https://www.riverchessassociation.co.uk/news/91/57/Sewage-Updates.html.

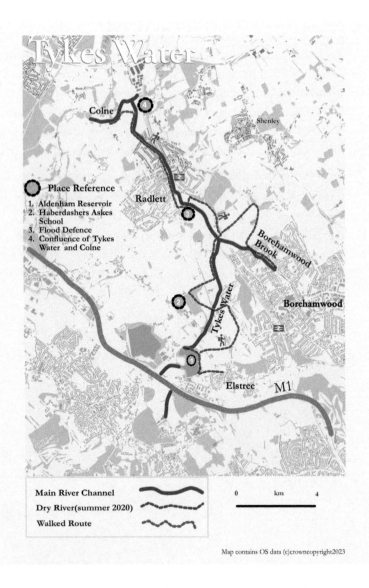

Route Map for Tykes Water

6. Tykes Water –
a reservoir of possibilities

Tykes Water is not much longer than 10km, a short often inaccessible tributary of the river Colne. For all its modest size it feeds a major body of water, the Aldenham Reservoir. I walked there from Elstree to begin the day's trek. The actual headwaters of Tykes Water are a network of drainage ditches south of the reservoir and the A41.

Aldenham Reservoir was originally hand-dug by French prisoners during the Napoleonic Wars (1795–7) to serve the future Grand Junction of the Grand Union Canal. While it has long been a popular public recreation area, its future for walking, swimming, fishing and sailing feels uncertain. It looked like asset stripping, but with no 'strategic need' for the reservoir British Waterways sold it to private investors back in 1992. Hertfordshire County Council gave up a lease on adjoining land in 2015, establishing a not-for-profit community enterprise company to run the site, and a circular walk of the lake was stopped up and fencing erected in 2020.

The owner's inspection of the reservoir raised concerns about the dam's stability and they dropped water levels to reduce pressure on the structure. The Council and residents objected to the adverse effects on plant, aquatic and animal life as well as amenities and the structure itself. The sailing club, no longer able to sail, handed back its lease in 2020. Planning applications for development, firstly for 150 dwellings, to fund repairs of the dam, were submitted but rejected as unjustified given the site's Green Belt status. Responding to a local residents' campaign, 'Save Aldenham Reservoir',[39]. Hertsmere Council in December 2021 identified the area as an 'Asset of Community Value'. Now if the owners sell the site, there must be opportunity for the local community to

....
39 Save Aldenham Reservoir, https://www.facebook.com/savealdenhamreservoir/.

purchase. A cross-party motion of Hertsmere Council in January 2022 included possible compulsory purchase of the site. Following appeals, the disputed circular path around the reservoir is at least now an official right of way.

In spite of its problems, I much enjoyed this large open expanse of water with all its birdlife (photo 14). I went on to try and locate Tykes Water but, as anticipated, found for the most part that it's hidden away passing through private land, including Haberdashers' Aske's School. A main outlet of the reservoir flows north to the school's grounds and into the man-made Tykes Water Lake. Judging from photographs it's an attractive body of water, so much so that its bridge was used in the opening sequences of the 1960s TV hit *The Avengers*. I followed a series of footpaths away from the river until I finally reached local public byway 79, Tykes Water Lane, which follows its channelled course and is a reasonable body of flowing water.

14. Aldenham Reservoir.

Before the town of Radlett, the river is again off limits. I had to walk on a road when an off-road path seems quite feasible (map 8). It would be part of a route linking Aldenham Reservoir to Radlett via Tykes Water Lane. The topography changes as the Tykes Water, here known as The Brook, runs into a valley. The secondary Tykes Water, or Borehamwood Brook, runs down from Borehamwood where it was dammed to create the ornamental lakes at Aberford Park. This strengthens the flow of the Tykes Water on its approach to Radlett. A £4m flood alleviation scheme was completed in 2003 to hold the Tykes Water back upstream and has reduced the flood risk. Radlett suffered badly in 1992, when around fifty homes were affected; a more recent rainstorm in 2014 resulted in limited localised flooding damaging two homes. One factor identified in a report on the latest flooding was rapid surface water run-off from local urbanised areas. It highlights a wider problem of hard surfacing, mostly for car use, in our urban environments. Not only have we paved land for roads and car parks, as we catered for ever higher car ownership, but we have also seen gardens lost under concrete paving, three million front gardens were paved over in the decade 2005 – 2015[40]. Cumulatively these impacts on amenity, biodiversity and flooding become very significant. It's a trend that exacerbates urban heating with climate change. Anyone who has tried to extend the front of their home will know planning permission was needed and was scrutinised in a public process – but front garden hard surface parking has long been 'permitted development' under planning regulations.[41] These provisions are outdated and not fit for current purposes.

....

40 Royal Horticultural Society 2015. Greening Grey Britain https://www.rhs.org.uk/communities/archive/PDF/Greener-Streets/greening-grey-britain-report.pdf
41 Planning Portal, 'Paving your front garden'. https://www.planningportal.co.uk/permission/common-projects/paving-your-front-garden/planning-permission.

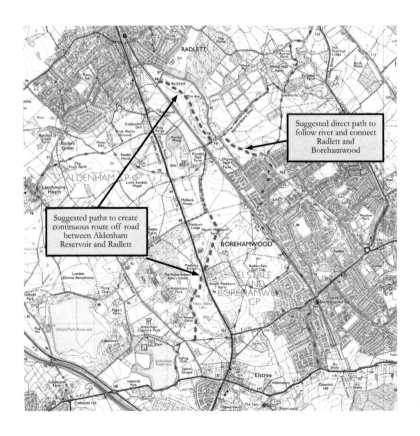

Suggested direct path to follow river and connect Radlett and Borehamwood

Suggested paths to create continuous route off road between Aldenham Reservoir and Radlett

Map 8

We should incentivise rainwater harvesting and sustainable drainage. It eases the burden and potential overload on our Victorian sewerage system that by design combines foul water sewers with surface water run-off. This weakens any case for 'exceptional circumstances' in heavy rains to justify raw sewage discharges. A win–win programme of action is possible. For a start we could be looking to introduce price incentives in the UK to retain rainwater as it falls. One company estimates the roof of the average UK home could collect 64,000 litres a year, that's 175 litres a day.42 In Germany, to shift the balance, stormwater fees43 are calculated based on the amount of hard surface area on a property.

My footpath went under the Midland Mainline railway to emerge into one of the largest green spaces beside the Tykes Water, an area of land owned by Aldenham Parish Council. The stream here had a wider gravel bed more typical of chalk stream morphology. The Tykes Water flows on in a deep cutting through the centre of Radlett, largely hidden from the high street or any other public view. I took a lunch break in Radlett Gardens just off the high street. The Tykes Water is revealed next alongside the main road at Tykeside Green, a tree-lined space with several giant floral displays. It's the first green space on entry from the north, also owned and maintained by the Parish Council.

The river swings north-west diverting under the A5, the Old Watling Street. The path here links easily with the town and is well used, as it takes you out into open fields. Work to shore up the footpath river edge with gabion walls has been undertaken. For a chalk stream, the Tykes Water still remains in a deep channel and not, as would be ideal, as a wide lateral flowing river that spreads across its floodplain. I followed the river down to where it bolsters the much-depleted river Colne near Colney Street, and then heads down to the Thames.

The Tykes Water isn't so long and is quite a heavily engineered stream. It feeds and anchors the Aldenham Reservoir which needs to be fully safeguarded for the public. On reflection, a broader strategy is needed to connect the reservoir with Radlett and the London Loop (map 9). The Tykes Water would certainly benefit from a wider programme of river

....

42 Impact Services. Rainwater recovery https://impact-services.co.uk/renewables/rainwater-recovery/

43 Darla Nickel, Wenke Schoenfelder, Dale Medearis, David P. Dolowitz, Melissa Keeley and William Shuster (2013), 'German experience in managing stormwater with green infrastructure', *Journal of Environmental Planning and Management*. http://dx.doi.org/10.1 080/09640568.2012.748652.

restoration and rewilding. I have set out suggestions and possibilities for a Tykes Water Trail that would better connect the river and reservoir, giving healthier options for those who wish to walk and cycle there from homes in the area. These paths would increase public access and appreciation of the Tykes Water itself.

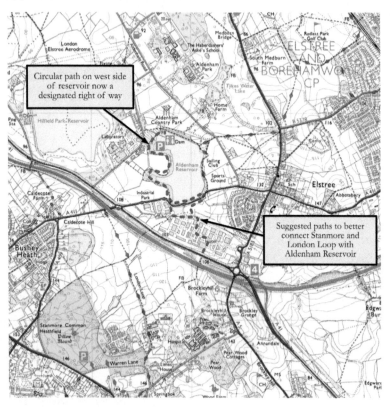

Map 9

'Now pitch in old fellow' said the Rat.

Western Hertfordshire

Main Towns

1. Hemel Hempstead
2. Watford
3. Luton
4. St Albans
5. Borehamwood
6. Hitchin
7. Letchworth
8. Stevenage
9. Welwyn Garden City
10. Royston
11. Hertford
12. Ware
13. Cheshunt
14. Bishops Stortford

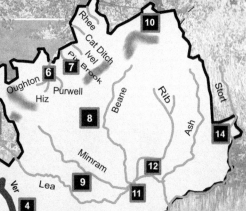

Cambridgeshire

Bedfordshire

Buckinghamshire

Essex

Greater London

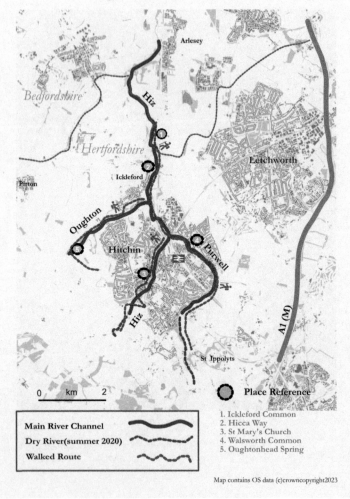

Route Map for Hiz Oughton and Purwell

7. The Hiz, Oughton and Purwell – our friends heading north

Within a northern strip of Hertfordshire lies the steeper scarp slope of the Chilterns. From here several chalk streams flow north into Bedfordshire and Cambridgeshire. Three river sources are located close to the town of Hitchin: the Purwell, the Oughton and the river Hiz. The confluence of the three is just north of Hitchin at Ickleford. They unite in the Hiz which runs through the town centre.

Hitchin was founded in the post-Roman era, in a period when society fragmented into local tribes. Many failed to survive but the Saxon Hicca tribe endured and gave Hitchin its name around AD 660. The settlement was well placed, sheltered by the Chilterns with reliable water sources and on England's oldest highway, the chalk ridge spine of the Icknield Way. The Icknield Way dates back up to 8,000 years ago, and its pathways link Dorset in the south-west to the Yorkshire Wolds in the north.

Hitchin prospered then as now as a market town, and was boosted by King Offa of Mercia establishing an early Benedictine church there in AD 795. When Danish invaders settled to the north, the town had to pay the 'Danegeld' tax to avoid attack – protection money rackets for the Middle Ages.

The river Oughton is a short tributary which feeds the river Hiz from the west, rising from its spring at Oughtonhead. From this deep wooded cutting, a path follows a gentle flow north-east via Oughtonhead Common, a local nature reserve on the boundary of Hitchin parish. The Oughton, Purwell and Hix rivers meet to the north of Hitchin at Ickleford and meander north through Ickleford Common where the water opens out into a wide river meadow. The combined flow of the Oughton, Purwell and Hiz makes for a healthy body of water and plentiful clear flows with a rich aquatic and insect life. Plants include long trailing spring water crowfoot; mammals such as the water shrew and birds such as kingfishers also find their home here. The Hicca Way[44] is a long-distance walking path that follows the Hiz north up to its confluence with the river Ivel in Bedfordshire, taking the route that the Hicca people may have traversed with their payments of bread to the Vikings. It could stay closer to the Hiz from Ickleford Common (map 10).

Map 10

....
44 Ickleford Parish Council, 'The Hicca Way'. https://ickleford-pc.gov.uk/the-parish/the-hicca-way/.

Retracing my steps, I picked up the route of the river Hiz back into Hitchin, noting how the river is sometimes prominent while at other times not, such as when it gets lost around the Sainsbury's supermarket. The river is placed in a man-made pool of water in the town centre amidst the church, the market and a large surface car park. St Mary's Church Hitchin, the largest parish church in Hertfordshire, opens out onto the river. Its siting follows the Saxon minster and its size demonstrates the wealth of the medieval town. This canalised section of river operates via a balancing tank which, with the use of sluice gates, helps retain river water levels to create a visually appealing and deeper river as a setting for the church. With a level grass bank to one side, it is a popular communal area and well cared for, annually drained of silt, sludge and general rubbish by the local council.

Opposite the church is St Mary's car park. Once an area of squalid yards and slum housing, this was cleared in the 1930s. An 1849 report highlighted its appalling squalor and disease[45] and a shamed town took action introducing new sanitation. In 1858 a storm resulted in sewer system overload and sewage backing up out of domestic taps, the worst-case scenario now frequently given to justify sewage spills. The size and dominance of car parking along the river detracted from the scene and the historic character. How much better this site could be as a piece of townscape with a landscaped green. The attachment to big car parks is a common problem for small market towns grappling in the face of poor public transport services and car-dependent visitors.

The river Hiz was out of bounds, as it ran through the private grounds of the former Hitchin Priory. Any chance of a path? (map 11). I had to walk along a local road to reach Charlton where the well head is found. Signs told of a campaign to save the Windmill, a community riverside pub. With Council support the building secured designation as an Asset

....
45 S. Williams, 'Slum housing in Hitchin, 1850s–1930s'. https://www.hertsmemories.org.uk/content/herts-history/towns-and-villages/hitchin/slum-housing-in-hitchin-1850s-1930s.

of Community Value, and in 2022 new ownership plans and reopening were announced. Good to hear. Not far beyond is the final walk to the river well head and the source of the Hiz. When I got there, I could see it had the right morphology, but probably because it was the end of August, it lacked any water. The waymarking for the well heads of both Oughton and Hiz could be improved for those not so used to finding their way by Ordnance Survey. I suspect many pass by not realising what they are.

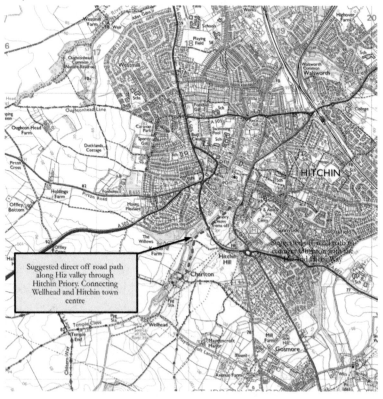

Map 11

The third stream of Hitchin is the Purwell, fed by two local brooks coming down from high ground around St Ippolyts. A first section of the river is visible and accessible on a walking path along the southern edge of Hitchin, and then the river enters Purwell Meadows and Walsworth Common. These are popular spots for locals and day visitors, who can enjoy the combination of a peaceful meadow and a naturally meandering river. Hertfordshire County Council Countryside Management Service has been focusing its efforts in chalk river restoration on Purwell Meadows and Walsworth Common in Hitchin, working with the landowner, North Hertfordshire District Council. There are recreational areas for children and the Millstream pub that sits on the river just between them seemed to be doing good business.

North of Walsworth Common the Purwell meets the Hiz then disappears beneath a couple of railway lines before confluence with the Oughton. I slightly lost the official path and hacked my way through overgrown shrubbery, passing under the impressively massive brick railway arches of the Great Northern line (photo 15). I finally returned to my car, detouring to locate the also dried-up source of the Purwell. I finished the day enjoying the colours of a summer sunset from the grounds of St Ippolyts Norman Parish Church on top of a Chiltern hill.

15. Hiz flows under Great Northern.

This is the variety that is Hertfordshire. With streams flowing north and a steep north-facing escarpment, here it feels part of a different landscape. Those who historically drew up the county boundaries of Hertfordshire and Bedfordshire probably didn't worry too much about topographical neatness – or were they also looking to divide the territory and influence of the Hicca folk? Just being mischievous. Hitchin long remained one of the larger historic market towns in the county, but it was Hertford and St Albans that assumed the greater status.

A complete river Hiz trail through the town will take a lot more detailed redevelopment work, given how often the river has been encroached by building and private land. The Hiz enjoys the Hicca Way that takes you along the river when it can. I've made suggestions (maps 10 and 11) for future additions, including a link from the river Oughton way to connect the routes better before they turn north.

River Ivel and Cat Ditch

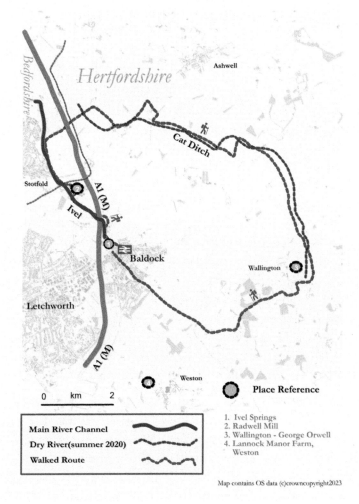

Route Map for Ivel and Cat Ditch

8. The Ivel and the Cat Ditch – the lost streams of the north

I decided to combine my walk along the river Ivel with the Cat Ditch; both lie on the northern edge of Hertfordshire. It was a circular walk starting from Baldock, a town founded in the twelfth century by the Knights Templar and also close to the Icknield Way.

The river Ivel, when full and healthy, flows from Ivel Springs Local Nature Reserve, just north of Baldock. It runs only 3km in Hertfordshire, then into Bedfordshire joining the river Ouse, and eventually reaches the North Sea at Kings Lynn. Ivel Springs is owned by North Hertfordshire District Council and was once a place of watercress production. Local volunteer work by the Friends of Baldock Green Spaces has restored the site. The river dried up in 2019 before a recovery of sorts and in August 2020 I observed some water as I walked. Sadly, in 2022, the headwaters of the Ivel completely dried up and retreated. Local group The Revival Association,[46] part of the Chalk Aquifer Alliance (a network of grassroot chalk stream groups) is campaigning for its recovery and demanding the local water company, Affinity, and the Environment Agency limit abstraction and help replenish the aquifers. A lead voice of the Chalks Stream Coalition CaBA strategy, Charles Rangley Wilson, has described the Ivel as a 'basket case' due to the amounts of water being taken.[47]

One goal of the Revival Association is the restoration of sufficient flow in the upper river Ivel 'to sustain brown trout all year round'. A good standard to aim for. Currently Affinity Water can abstract up to 14.8 million litres a day. Revival commissioned an expert report in June 2022, which estimated groundwater levels in the Upper Ivel had fallen between three and six metres since the 1890s. It noted the Ivel Springs

---

46 The Revival Association, https://www.revivel.org/.
47 Adam Vaughan, 'The plight of chalk streams in England', *The Times*, 14 March 2023. https://www.revivel.org/latest-news/times-article-on-the-plight-of-chalk-streams-in-england

and Nortonbury Springs would historically have flowed perennially, supporting watermills. It calculated that abstraction in the Upper Ivel catchment is about 50% of the average catchment recharge, putting it amongst the most heavily abstracted chalk streams in the country. They are calling for water to be taken further downstream from Grafham Reservoir and for abstraction from the head of the Ivel to be reduced to about 10% of the catchment recharge, down to about 2.4 million litres a day. I hope somebody is listening to them!

My walk took me from the Ivel Springs area to a narrow footway along a busy A507 before turning down Norton Mill Lane under the A1(M). Here I got onto the 'Kingfisher Way', a 20-mile walking route that tracks the length of the Ivel as it goes down to Bedfordshire and joins the Ouse. The water levels were low here, although historically sections of this river powered the Norton mill and Norton trout fisheries held waters deep enough for fishing boats. Quite hard to imagine. I reached the boundary of Hertfordshire at Radwell Mill with its large millpond, now a dwelling. This marks the current upper extent of the river in severely reduced years. The remains of a Roman villa at Radwell, a scheduled ancient monument,[48] appears to be sited at a location of pre-Roman settlement. Neolithic people enjoyed and valued the holy waters long before the Romans; the remnants of a bathhouse reveal the glamour of bathing in the river Ivel.

On my walk I circled east to get back into Hertfordshire and follow the Cat Ditch. Traffic noise from the A1 meant it never seemed too far away. The public footpath led me to a point with no facilitated crossing of the motorway to link the footpaths either side. I crossed it carefully. When I reached the Cat Ditch, it was mostly dry for its section in Hertfordshire. It is known to be seasonal. The lack of water was unexpected given that the Cat Ditch is drawn from such a wide area of farmland running up to chalk uplands near Therfield and Sandon. Groundwater levels must

....

48 Historic England, 'Radwell Roman villa'. https://historicengland.org.uk/listing/the-list/list-entry/1016308?section=official-list-entry.

have been low – presumably the combined effects of over-abstraction and a modern rapidly drained agricultural landscape. The walk led me into the peaceful village of Newnham where I stopped for some lunch in the churchyard. I found the grave of one Arthur Farr, a son of the Manor killed just six weeks before the end of World War II. A friend had told me his great-aunt had been a likely match for Arthur, and if he'd lived then my friend might have had high family connections here.

The Cat Ditch runs south across private farmland so my only way to follow it was along Cat Ditch Lane, which at least was reasonably quiet. It was a gentle steady climb up to the streams marked source at Wallington. Here I found a pool of mud and an old oak tree. The celebrated writer George Orwell lived in the village for a few years before the war, married in the local church and used some local references in writing *Animal Farm*. I'm not sure if the Cat Ditch gets a reference and wonder how healthy it was in his time here.

Of special note among the farms in the chalk hills south of Baldock is Lannock Manor Farm, Weston. Since 2010 it has been practising and promoting no-till farming, or what is broadly termed 'regenerative agriculture'. The Cherry brothers host an annual Groundswell[49] event which attracts hundreds of farmers and food producers, who come to learn and discuss the theory and application of conservation agriculture. It is excellent news, and not just for wider ecology and the climate – it really matters for healthy chalk streams too. Rapid water run-off from farms and fields increases when the soil surface is left bare, as is common in orthodox farming practice with heavy ploughing and an over-reliance on fertilisers. John Cherry explained how if the soil surface is undisturbed, it increases the diversity of soil pore networks, the range of pore sizes and their connectedness, which in turn increases biodiversity. Not only do you achieve carbon-rich, more fertile soils, but it also improves water retention. The soil being able to capture rain, slow

---

49 Groundswell is part of a global movement promoting farming systems that use the principles of regenerative agriculture. https://groundswellag.com/mission-statement/.

run-off and allow rainwater to infiltrate down into the chalk aquifers also reduces flood risks downstream. Farming in this way can increase the 'effective rainfall', the rain that actually soaks down into the ground and replenishes the aquifer.

Furthermore, as no-till farming allows soils to recover and be enriched by organic matter, it also increases their carbon content, the kind of 'carbon capture' that really does work. I heard of a carbon neutral (actually carbon negative) farm in Northamptonshire featured on the BBC radio series *39 Ways to Save the Planet*.[50] In eighteen years, the farm has nearly doubled the carbon content of its soil, from 3.8% to 6.7%. While the change of methods has to be sustained long term, this can potentially have huge benefits if rolled out on a wider scale. Globally it is estimated the soil holds about 2.5–5% of carbon emissions.

Farmers who understand these benefits for the environment and all the chalk streams such as the Ivel and Cat Ditch are acting on their own initiative. They do not currently get paid or incentivised to undertake such strategies by government. A promised Environmental Land Management Scheme (ELMS) may do so, to encourage more of what seems a win–win for the earth, wildlife, for climate action and locally for Hertfordshire's chalk streams. Regenerative farming techniques over chalk catchments are fully supported by Revivel, who also hope they can be embedded in the national ELMS strategies proposed by DEFRA.

In its latest plan, Affinity Water Company says it will undertake a feasibility study on reduced borehole abstraction at Baldock and Letchworth. It may be a pilot scheme. A key principle of Chalk Streams First is to limit abstraction in the headwaters, and it's encouraging that Ofwat has now given this its explicit support. Huge reductions are needed for the Ivel and Cat Ditch to flow again.

....
50 'Zero Carbon Farm', 39 Ways to Save the Planet, BBC Radio 4. http://www.listenersguide.
org.uk/bbc/podcast/episode/?p=m000qwt3&e=m000vjnp.

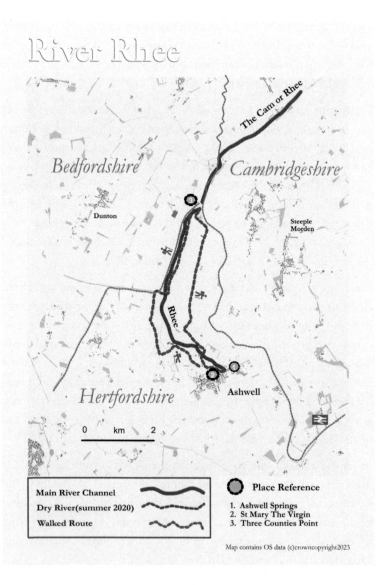

Route Map for Rhee

9. The Rhee – the playful spring of Ashwell

The Rhee is a tributary of the river Cam and runs 6km north from its source in Ashwell to the county boundary and then on to Cambridge. The magic of the river Rhee (pronounced as in 'see') is how it rises as a spring in the very heart of Ashwell village, North Hertfordshire. The name of the village is derived from the Anglo-Saxon words for 'ash' and 'spring'. Archaeological finds from a nearby Iron Age settlement and gilded offerings to the Goddess Senuna mean the Rhee too was probably viewed as an ancient sacred river.[51] We're following the ancestors.

In my walk around Hertfordshire, I usually searched for the source of chalk streams, but rarely found water. They were frequently inaccessible, dry or both. Here, albeit with an augmented flow to safeguard its natural interest, the waters emerge in a fully public place at Ashwell Springs. It's a popular wooded amphitheatre off the main high street and a Site of Special Scientific Interest.

The spring was gifted back in 1972 by Whitbreads, owners of the former Fordham's Brewery in Ashwell which closed after a hundred years of brewing in the village. Water for the brewery had been taken direct from Ashwell spring. While not immune to the impacts of abstraction, water flows here are, as they should be, clear, unpolluted and at a constant temperature even during the coldest winters and at recent times of drought. As a place for recreation, it is wonderful and possibly a closely guarded secret. For those who know, it must be an irresistible draw on a nice day. A space for children to play happily and paddle safely in the water, and for families to meet. A place of many good memories, such as those I witnessed on the hot summer's day (photo 16) I walked the river Rhee with my friend Ken, a resident of Ashwell.

....
51   Jonathan Spain's Blog, 'River Rhee – an ancient sacred river?'. https://jonathanspain. wordpress.com/2012/01/30/river-rhee-an-ancient-sacred-river/.

16. Ashwell Springs.

We felt a bit old and overdressed to play in the spring water ourselves so after a short pause to admire the scene we took off southwards, passing through the parish churchyard of St Mary the Virgin. It's an imposing and distinctive fourteenth-century medieval church built in a local white limestone known as 'Clunch'. The stone is sufficiently strong to build with, but doesn't weather well, thus requiring regular repair. The tower to the spire only has clockfaces on three sides. Ken explained that a fourth was avoided as the nearby landowner was concerned his farmworkers, or serfs, would turn into 'clock watchers' and not work hard enough if they could see the time from the adjacent field.

In 2013, the church, which used to chime every quarter-hour through the night, became the centre of a nationally reported row after complaints from new residents. The chiming clock, installed in 1898, was turned off for eighteen months while repairs were carried out and new residents moved in seemingly unaware. North Hertfordshire District Council (NHDC) was legally obliged to investigate and ruled that the chimes were 'prejudicial to health' and had to be silenced between 11pm and 6am. Initially it meant turning off the chimes altogether but by May 2015, after an appeal for funding, a timer had been installed. Now the church bells ring but fall silent overnight.

As we walked it appeared there were more opportunities for a footpath closer to the river through the village. Currently the water is out of view. It emerges by the radically altered mill house, probably one of the least successful pieces of conservation in a village that is otherwise extremely well preserved. Ken and I walked on into the open floodplain mostly drained for arable farming. From here with a modest investment, you could create an excellent walking route along the river up to the county boundary, one that could link up with a longer path along the Rhee and Cam to Cambridge. It might pass the village sewage works at Ashwell Farm, but no bad thing if it means more of the public keeping an eye on outfalls. Discharges out of sight are out of mind too? The river Rhee is classified by the Environment Agency as being in moderate ecological condition, with poor likelihood of being 'good' by 2027, and a fail for chemical classification.[52]

Relying on limited rights of way meant having to walk along the long straight lane, Northfield Road, which lacked any verge or parallel path. Fortunately, it was not too busy. We quite soon found ourselves at the northern tip of Hertfordshire, the only place where Hertfordshire meets with both Cambridgeshire and Bedfordshire. You wouldn't have known that if you didn't have a map, as there is nothing to explain or identify the cartographical significance of the location. Three Counties Radio might be interested, except for them it's the wrong three.[53] There was a large willow at this 'Three Counties' point offering welcome shade on a hot day. If footpaths were added, with bridge crossings as necessary, it would

....
52 UK Government, *River Rhee Catchment Data 2019*. https://environment.data.gov.uk/catchment-planning/WaterBody/GB105033038100.
53 BBC Three Counties Radio refers to Bedfordshire, Hertfordshire and Buckinghamshire.

be an attractive resting stop, part of a longer riverside trail of about two days leading down the river Cam and eventually to Cambridge. (We know because Ken and I went back and walked it later.)

It had been a short walk from Ashwell to reach the edge of Hertfordshire. We returned along the Rhee towards Ashwell, noting some trampled lines along the edge of fields already used by locals. So, for the return we decided to avoid the hazards of the road and take a route alongside the river. It worked fine without any undue impediment to farmland or disturbance of farm sites. These permissive paths would be a definite benefit for the village and for local walking (map 12).

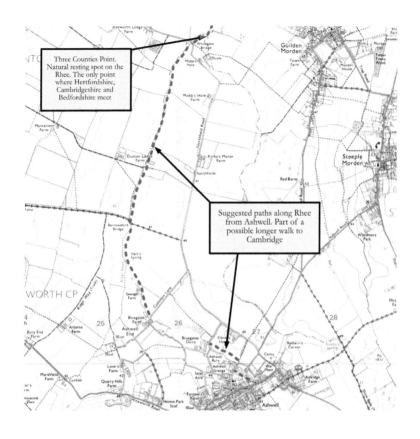

Three Counties Point.
Natural resting spot on the
Rhee. The only point
where Hertfordshire,
Cambridgeshire and
Bedfordshire meet

Suggested paths along Rhee
from Ashwell. Part of a
possible longer walk to
Cambridge

Map 12

Towards the end we looked south to Ashwell – any walker would be drawn by the view of the St Mary's church tower and spire, as at 54m high it's the tallest in Hertfordshire. There amidst its green oasis, it signalled both our destination and the direction of travel. It would be a fitting end for anyone walking up the river Cam/Rhee from Cambridge, especially if they can also enjoy regular sight of healthy river flows. One day, we hope.

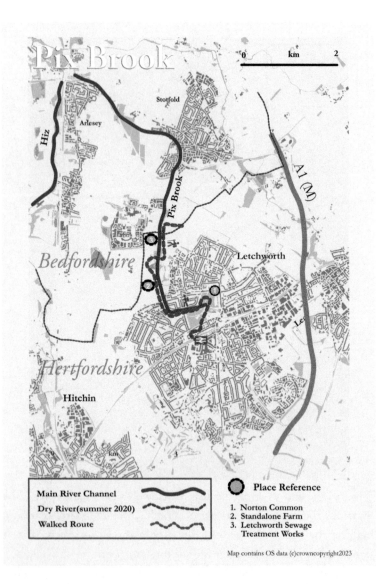

Route Map for Pix Brook

10. Pix Brook – from the heart of the world's first garden city

With a friend, Alan, and a local resident, Jenny, I set out from Letchworth station to find and follow the Pix Brook. It's another short river, 3km in length, in Hertfordshire. This one though rises within the large green space of Norton Common at the heart of Letchworth, the world's first garden city founded in 1903. The 60-acre common is a popular local nature reserve, mostly woodland with some long avenues. Once it was arable and grazing land, and there is evidence of earlier medieval ridge-and-furrow farming patterns. It lies north of the town centre, meeting the route of the Icknield Way which crosses east to west through Letchworth.

The common includes several leisure activities – a skate park, a bowls club and also an outdoor pool. It's not just well used, but feels owned by the town community. It has a Friends of Norton Common (FoNC) group of volunteers to champion it, who organise monthly work parties to clean out the brook.

The Pix Brook appeared to have several possible sources with a number of channels running through the common. Water run-off from surrounding areas would probably be part of the mix too. On inspection we noted what looked like a few unsuccessful attempts at river channel engineering with broken sections of concrete block, neither helping aquatic life nor looking good.

There were no access restrictions, so we were able to follow the Pix Brook all the way through the common and along paths laid out into the adjacent area of Pix Brook Meadows. The ease of the walking route was presumably all part of the original garden city planning. Families with young children were coming down to play around the river. Chalk streams are gentle waterways with a flow and shallow morphology ideally suited to the safe play spaces that children of all ages need. We found a swing with a rubber tyre hanging over the brook at one point, although as the water was quite depleted play here might have made for a hard landing.

The course of the river led us out of Letchworth's built-up area into the surrounding countryside. There is no right of way along the river by Standalone Farm, a working farm and leisure destination popular with young families. Fortunately, we met an employee of the Letchworth Heritage Foundation who own the land, who said it would be fine for us to walk along the river. Will this become a permissive path? ... or was it someone feeling permissive, generously allowing people to walk unimpeded given all the other restrictions on travel and socialising during the Covid year of 2020.

The river was in quite a deep channel as it went down the side of Standalone Farm. We picked up the route of the Greenway, a new 13-mile orbital walk of Letchworth with sections suitable for cycling and wheelchair use. Only a few years old, it's a great idea for any town or village. At this point it follows the Pix on its last section in Hertfordshire, taking it past the town's sewage works. Next to it is a flood storage reservoir and flood gates on the Pix Brook. It's managed by the Bedfordshire and River Ivel Internal Drainage Board (IDB), to reduce flood risks to downstream urban areas in mid-Bedfordshire.

Here we witnessed the gushing outfall of hopefully treated water from the Letchworth Sewage Treatment Works (Anglian Water). However, as we could see without any scientific analysis, the river was clearly suffering. A heavy algae layer glistened in the bright sunshine; it wasn't flowing, it was nutrient rich and there was a strong smell (photo 17). Newspaper accounts from 2016–17 suggest the odours had been worse then, and back in 2009 Anglian Water were fined £75,000 for sewage spills.

17. Algae by Letchworth STW.

Maybe the situation has improved? The Rivers Trust website[54] reported no spills at all to Pix Brook from these works in the year 2021. Even without spills there may be issues of nutrient enrichment, usually phosphates that suffocate aquatic life. Treatment works vary in their ability to remove phosphates from the returned water. Unless volunteers carry it out, there is no regular public monitoring to show the streams' immediate ecological and chemical condition.

It's a huge works for a small river. Letchworth has a population of 33,000 and is being expanded. A Green Belt site for 900 houses allocated to the north will break the greenway. Even with the best water conservation provisions and sustainable drainage designs, if we recognise the finite limits to the environment and water use, does major development at this location make strategic sense? Abstraction has to be reduced but

....
54 In 2021, this sewer storm overflow to the Pix Brook spilled 0 times for a total of 0 hours, discharging into the Pix Brook. https://theriverstrust.org/key-issues/sewage-in-rivers.

if water is pumped from elsewhere to compensate for it, that only adds to energy costs.

The Pix Brook leaves Hertfordshire before its confluence with the river Ivel. The Ivel flows on northwards through Biggleswade down to the Great Ouse. Potential Environment Agency funds were reported in the news[55] to address flooding risks along the Pix Brook. Separately a Pix Brook Watercourse project has highlighted the need to address heavy shading of the stream, overly steep banks, blockages and outdated concrete structures at Norton Common. The coalition of groups behind the Chalk Stream Restoration Strategy are helping to bolster the knowledge and skills around the naturalising of chalk streams. For an area like Norton Common, in community ownership and with its active friends, this gives hope. Indeed, Jenny has reported that since the walk in 2020 a lot of conservation work at the common has benefited tributaries of the brook, though water levels in the river remain disappointingly low. If abstraction is reduced in these upper chalk stream areas and there is investment in the treatment works and continuing river restoration, then the prospects are good for the river and its ecology.

....

55 BBC News, 'Pix Brook: flood risk area is shortlisted for £6m grant', 11 January 2022.
    https://www.bbc.co.uk/news/uk-england-beds-bucks-herts-59952877.

*'I am Toad, the motor car snatcher, the
prison breaker, the Toad who always escapes'*

Eastern Hertfordshire

Main Towns

1. Hemel Hempstead
2. Watford
3. Luton
4. St Albans
5. Borehamwood
6. Hitchin
7. Letchworth
8. Stevenage
9. Welwyn Garden City
10. Royston
11. Hertford
12. Ware
13. Cheshunt
14. Bishops Stortford

Cambridgeshire

Bedfordshire

Buckinghamshire

Essex

Greater London

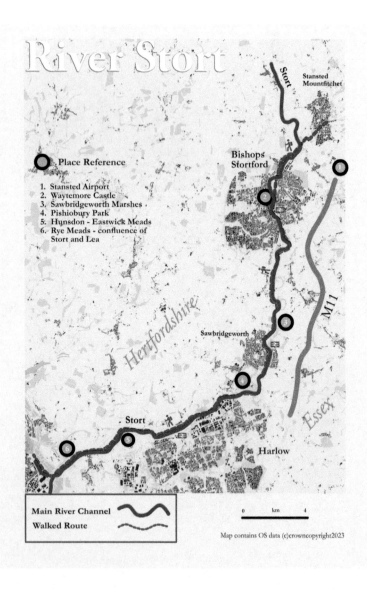

Route Map for Stort

11. The Stort – a green travel route or an unsustainable growth corridor?

The head of the Stort is just outside the county boundary near to Langley in Essex. When it flows it meanders ten miles through Essex first and then reaches Hertfordshire south of Stansted Mountfitchet. The Stort is the most easterly of Hertfordshire's rivers and as I realised provides one of its best long-distance river walks. It forms part of a group of six rivers in eastern Hertfordshire that merge in the river Lea and flow to the Thames.

A good length of the river was canalised by 1769, reaching as far as Bishops Stortford. Train travel to Stortford arrived with record rapid times in the 1840s and was improved by its electrification in the mid-1980s. The controversial 1984 decision to choose Stansted as London's third airport brought major development impacts in the 'M11 growth corridor' between London and Cambridge. The airport continues to expand. Uttlesford Council had costs awarded against it in 2021 for 'unreasonably' refusing expansion on climate grounds.[56] The Council has been criticised[57] but surely the root problem is incoherent and illogical government policy. How can limiting the most damaging emissions to the planet in a declared climate emergency be unreasonable?

The river towpath is walked and cycled but like others it needs upgrading and regular maintenance to be more suited for multi-modal travel. The Stort is well placed to be one of the county's best sustainable travel corridors, albeit road and air traffic is present.

....

56 Flight Free, 'The sad case of Stansted Airport', 7 October 2021. https://flightfree.co.uk/post/the-sad-case-of-stansted-airport/.

57 BBC News, 'Stansted Airport: council criticised for rejecting expansion plan', 15 July 2022. https://www.bbc.co.uk/news/uk-england-essex-62180461.

I took the train to Stansted Mountfitchet, Essex, to walk the river with my friend Jane, a local resident. I often compare the merits of train and car journeys. I love the train for its environmental efficiency and friendliness. It has a quarter of the emissions, reduces noise, air and water pollution, and when used helps free up congested roads. However, this journey cost me five times the fuel cost of driving. Pollution pays! The train offers more flexibility for walks, stress-free travel and better views, so I paid – but why doesn't travel pricing support climate-friendly habits?

The river Stort is certainly one of the best used in Hertfordshire, though not so much below Stansted Mountfitchet where it is little more than a large stream. The footpaths in Essex felt less connected, less well used and less maintained. It's something of a vicious circle. I mused on this while walking in shorts through dense nettles, which numbed the lower limbs for a while.

Into Hertfordshire, the Stort flows under the A120 bypass north of Bishops Stortford and the path and river valley widen out into the Bat Willow Hurst Country Park. It's a little-used northern gateway to the town and the first part of its luxuriant green spine focused on the Stort. The park includes drainage ponds to capture rainwater falling on development areas north of the town, which then filter slowly into the river Stort. It's an all too rare example of the sustainable drainage that we need to apply consistently to slow rainwater run-off. This is good for nature, helps replenish groundwater levels, reduces flood risks and alleviates the pressures on our combined sewer system. When I worked on local planning applications, as officers we often felt the sustainable drainage provisions weren't good enough, lacking rainwater capture, natural filtration, green roofs etc. The national policy context and responses of the Environment Agency didn't support more rigorous demands. The Flood and Water Management Act 2010 (Schedule 3) had provisions to remove developers' automatic right to connect rainwater drainage from new development to combined sewers but was never enacted in England (Wales did in 2019). Suds provisions will hopefully become mandatory in 2024 as part of the response to the arguments on sewage spills,[58] but it's clearly been resisted by the lobbying of housebuilders resulting in at least thirteen wasted years.

Waterside Stortford is developing a sequence of green spaces north to south through the heart of Bishops Stortford, the town which gave its name to the river. We walked through Grange Paddocks, with its new swimming pool and leisure centre, which leads to the town centre meads. The wetlands here were probably cleared by the Saxons and the Normans, who built a motte-and-bailey defence. Waytemore Castle is a Grade I listed building and ancient monument, although there are few remains visible beyond the earth mound. I know Bishops Stortford well from nearly thirty years' planning work at East Hertfordshire, but what a day in the summer sunshine of 2020. Seeing families outside, enjoying the expanse of nature and bumping into former work colleagues I'd not seen in years (as you do when you walk). I had probably never enjoyed a walk through the town so much.

Bishops Stortford had a maltings industry too that benefited from early canal building. The town may not have been the end of the navigation if a proposed canal link north up to Cambridge and the Norfolk Broads had been built to connect with London. Survey work was carried out but the funds were never there for what was a very ambitious and speculative project.

The Stort waters appeared deep and mirror-like. Although it's a highly modified chalk stream, it is well regarded for its ecological value and wildlife. It's also a tranquil location for houseboats, which are there in good numbers all the way down to the confluence with the river Lea.

....
58   Weightmans LLP, 'Are we on the verge of proper implementation of a sustainable drainage system regime in England?', September 2022. https://www.lexology.com/library/detail. aspx?g=7925d294-f020-423c-8c40-076320071213.

The towpath provides full access for houseboat residents as well as those who seek to enjoy the river and its canal for leisure.

I pressed on south of the town. The river is paralleled by the Stansted Express railway line with the occasional swish of a passing train (photo 18). Overhead is also the intermittent roar of planes following, in theory, their approved Stansted flightpaths. Many cyclists understandably wish to enjoy the Stort but its path is a bit narrow and I had to pause to let people pass. Widening and resurfacing would make sense for all users, as well as designing better crossing points in Stortford.

18. Stort near Spellbrook.

The river towpath passes close to the Sawbridgeworth Marshes, one of the best examples of retained wetland habitat owned and managed by the Essex Wildlife Trust. It escaped the era of land drainage. Its reedbeds are good habitat for singing warblers and flowering marsh plants, and there's a chance to spot water voles too.

At Pishiobury Park, south of Sawbridgeworth, boardwalks along the Stort link the river neatly to this public park and also provide sociable resting places in shady areas, essential as we adapt to a heating climate. Moving on I bumped into the son of a good friend who lives on the river – unfortunately his boat had been broken into. It was in for repairs at the Keckys Farm site.

Rowneybury House can be seen from the river, but is no longer home to the Beckhams. 'Beckingham Palace' as the papers dubbed it. As I recall our planning enforcement team had to cope with some feverish interest when some outbuildings went up there without planning permission.

Reaching Harlow, the river is not far from industry but you wouldn't have known it. The ambience is quite natural. Gibberd's 1947 master plan for the new town certainly sought to safeguard Temple Fields as a green wedge separating the river and the new town, although in practice the Harlow industrial zone, now mostly retail, cars and warehousing, crept much closer to the river extending north of the railway line. Not far from here is the neglected site of a Roman temple and the location of the first pre-Roman settlement near Harlow Mill. Perhaps future planning will give the heritage more respect and connect it better to the Stort Valley, which is after all the original reason people settled here.

Huge expansions for a 'garden town' into the countryside north of the Stort are being planned. This is top-down numbers-driven planning with huge Green Belt land releases. Highly regrettable in the view of many, including myself. Nonetheless a number of attractive new walking spaces along the river have been created at Harlow, and could development be the impetus to safeguard them and connect them sustainably with the rest of the town.

The Stort Valley Way is a circular route that goes along the Stort up to Sawbridgeworth and then circles back around Harlow. Without wishing to be too contentious, I would say that the Stort Valley Way ought to go all the way up the Stort Valley. Harlow can have its own circular path. There isn't much to do to create a waymarked trail all the way up to Stansted Mountfitchet and with some additions it could go to Clavering in Essex. It connects well with stations up and down the route.

Parndon Mill west of Harlow (photo 19) is a tranquil watery scene and one surviving watermill from many that were located on the river. A small community of craftsmen and artists has restored the mill and established itself here since the 1960s and its not hard to see why they were drawn to the location.[59] With its obvious attractions it will be interesting to see how well this area is managed and integrated with the garden town development. The most disturbed section of the walk was the traffic along the A414 as I moved west into the Eastwick and Hunsdon Meads. These are rare sites still managed under the ancient Lammas system. After a hay-cut on Lammas Day (11 August) commoners enjoy grazing rights through into winter. It's a unique unimproved grassland that in spring and summer has a colourful display of cowslip, buttercup and yellow rattle.

19. Parndon Mill scene.

....
59   Parndon Mill. A hub of creativity https://www.parndonmill.co.uk

Noise here, even with electric vehicles, will only reduce if traffic levels and vehicle speeds are lowered. This is a major challenge with the growth north of Harlow and a lot of associated road building. There is talk of a new east–west tram for Hertfordshire,[60] but will it happen in time for the new housing or arrive too late to influence travel patterns? Other countries (e.g. Germany, Sweden), as is well noted, do far better in securing investment in early good quality infrastructure.

Along the towpath I bagged myself a boxful of blackberries, fruit foraging that is freely and readily available but often overlooked in our busy lives. The last village I reached on the Stort was Roydon, a commuter village with its own railway station. West of here is an area of low-lying lakes including Roydon Mill Leisure Park with a large marina. Allegedly many of the marina's 300 houseboats are lived in, contrary to planning conditions, and a sewage facility at the site struggles to cope. A second reduced planning application for a further 168 berths, which also promised to widen the existing towpath, was refused in April 2022.

The river towpath takes you down to the meeting of the Stort and the Lea just below Rye House and the Rye Meads sewage works, also a RSPB site. It had been a great green walk, along a resplendent lived-in river, sociable with a few chance encounters. A little further investment in the Stort corridor will go a long way.

....
60   Hertfordshire County Council, Improving Passenger Transport – Hertfordshire Essex Rapid Transit. https://www.hertfordshire.gov.uk/services/highways-roads-and-pavements/ roadworks-and-road-closures/major-roadwork-projects/hert.aspx.

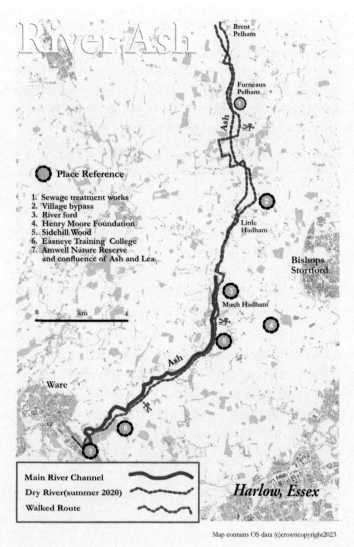

River Ash

Place Reference

1. Sewage treatment works
2. Village bypass
3. River ford
4. Henry Moore Foundation
5. Sidehill Wood
6. Easneye Training College
7. Amwell Nature Reserve
and confluence of Ash and Lea

Brent Pelham

Furneaux Pelham

Little Hadham

Bishops Stortford

Much Hadham

Ware

Ash

Harlow, Essex

Main River Channel	
Dry River(summer 2020)	
Walked Route	

Map contains OS data (c)crowncopyright2023

Route Map for Ash

12. The Ash –
all dried up with little left to go

Many of Hertfordshire's chalk streams are seasonal, dry in their upper reaches over the summer. This can provide unique habitats and be part of a natural cycle. However, lengthening dry periods and longer distances of dry channels are not healthy.

In the summer of 2020, drying up proved to be the case 'with knobs on' for the Ash. The source of the river is mapped as rising in chalk uplands near to Brent Pelham in East Hertfordshire. However, accompanied by Theo, a local walking friend, I found no water beyond an occasional small pool along the first 16km (10 miles) down to Much Hadham. That's over half the length of the river before its confluence with the Lea. I was shocked as I trudged down sections of a wide dry riverbed; it felt more like beach walking (see photo 20).

20. Dried up river Ash.

On a more positive note, some of the fields we followed had left uncultivated buffers along the watercourse. It's a simple measure that should be rolled out as standard good practice. It keeps chemicals away from river waters, allowing riparian habitats and wildlife to regenerate. The uncultivated wild fringe can also offer space for river restoration and new walking paths without affecting cultivated land. Public access to the river is quite limited in the upper sections of the Ash and I have made a few suggestions in hope that flows become re-established (map 13).

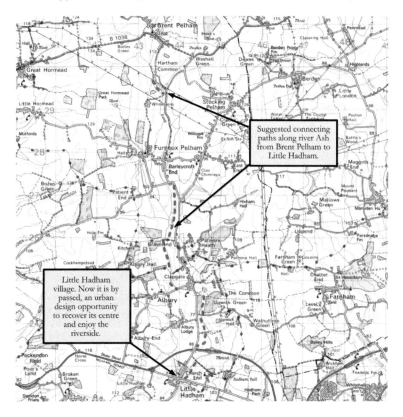

Suggested connecting paths along river Ash from Brent Pelham to Little Hadham.

Little Hadham village. Now it is by passed, an urban design opportunity to recover its centre and enjoy the riverside.

Map 13

The Ash in flow would be quite an asset for the Black Horse pub in Brent Pelham. The village of Furneaux Pelham has its own sewage treatment works in this dry upper section. It operates without being able to restore the flow of the river. Near to Albury we passed a small farm reservoir with an algal covering, presumably as nutrients seep through the ground with the use of fertilisers. No wildlife was evident but it provided some on-site water storage.`

The lack of water was painfully evident at Little Hadham too, with a dry riverbed alongside its old cottages. The village was once named Hadham Ashe after the river. Stane Street, a Roman road that linked London and Colchester, crossed here. East–west traffic has grown over the centuries with the A120 now providing a route to Stansted Airport and Bishops Stortford. During our walk a northern bypass for the A120 was under construction. It proved far from easy to negotiate. The bypass was finally opened in December 2021 and is anticipated to reduce through-village traffic from 18,000 to 5,000 vehicles a day.

Will that local benefit be sustained without other design or management measures? New road building is hugely expensive and makes no scientific sense in a climate emergency. The £40m cost here hopes to remove traffic from the village – the Little Hadham traffic lights were notorious for delays and tailbacks, as well as the many heavy lorries passing along the narrow main road. However, experience of bypasses elsewhere[61] shows overall traffic levels increase and often returns to the bypassed settlement.

The band Fairport Convention once lived in Little Hadham at the former Angel public house. Now, as lorries are removed, maybe it's time to remove through traffic entirely – a new village centre, with the return

....
61   CPRE, *The End of the Road March* 2017. https://www.cpre.org.uk/resources/the-end-of-the-road-challenging-the-road-building-consensus/. This called for a new smarter travel hierarchy. Its findings aligned with an earlier report by Friend of the Earth in 2006 on Newbury that traffic returned to pre bypass congestion levels after 9 years and overall increased by 50%

of a pub, music and conviviality? I hope the village, parish and local authorities monitor what happens in the post-bypass era and seize the opportunity to transform the centre. With good urban design a more people-friendly village seems possible. One element of this could be a restored riverside as a community meeting place.

The bypass was designed to create storage ponds that will hold up floodwaters of the Ash above the village. This will reduce downstream flood risk to the villages of Little Hadham and Hadham Ford, which experienced flooding most recently in 2001 and 2014.

Little Hadham once had a company selling spring water, which closed after a problem with contamination. At Church End Farm, just outside the village, Hadham Brewery makes award-winning malt beers using water drawn from its own borehole deep into the chalk aquifer. The amounts drawn aren't public knowledge. It's a reminder that there are over 18,000 private boreholes in England and Wales extracting at least 10.4 billion litres of water, and over 20,000 unlicensed abstractions (> 20 cubic metres a day). A 2022 Environment Agency whistleblower said most users are unmetered and the Agency can't reliably monitor them.[62] The system looks ripe for reform. It's critical if the root causes of chalk aquifer and groundwater depletion, by private abstractors as well as by main water companies, are to be addressed for the benefit of conservation.

Theo and I appreciated the public bench by the village sign and water pump in Hadham Ford, where we enjoyed our sandwiches. We walked away from the main valley road to get a bit closer to the river for a while, then came into Much Hadham at its north end, pausing in the grounds of its fine parish church. Much Hadham is a linear settlement aligned with the river Ash, and at 2km one of the longest villages in England.

---

62 Rachel Salvidge, 'Environment Agency has "no idea" how much water is taken, says whistleblower', *The Guardian*, 11 November 2022. https://www.theguardian.com/environment/2022/nov/11/environment-agency-has-no-idea-how-much-water-is-taken-says-whistleblower.

We found some flow to the river here and at Malting Lane crossed the old footbridge, one of a few places where the river Ash is forded. The ford becomes impassable in times of heavy rain and flooding. My friends Kate and Charlie, who grew up in Much Hadham, recall more water in the river back then, and being able to canoe in it. For Much Hadham youth, cycling through its flowing ford was a rite of passage; Charlie managed to fall in three times. Cars at night sometimes got stuck in the ford as their alcohol fuelled drivers misjudged the depth and strength of the river.

South of Much Hadham, the Ash valley sides were steeper and more wooded, as we passed the oak and hornbeam coppice beauty of Sidehill Wood and Mill Wood. Great places to enjoy bluebells in the springtime. There used to be watercress beds here at a point close to where the Bourne, a small tributary, joins the Ash from Perry Green. Perry Green was the last home and workshop of the modern British sculptor Henry Moore, and is now the site of the Henry Moore Foundation.

The path runs in the valley below Widford, passing a pumping station and sewage works. It forms part of the Hertfordshire Way, picking up the route of the old Buntingford branch railway. Much Hadham lost its station and rail service with the Beeching cuts in 1965. The village has seen a steady growth since and would have greatly benefited if the line could have been retained. It has surely only meant more traffic on narrow country lanes. Another false economy.

The river near Watersplace Farm was straightened when the train line from Stanstead Abbotts was built. Can a more natural river morphology be restored? The Herts and Middlesex Trust has a plan to improve water retention, water quality and habitat for water vole and trout here.[63] As the Ash passes on through the grounds of the Easneye Christian College, it winds around to provide one of the most attractive footpath walks

63   BBC News, 'Hertfordshire chalk rivers restoration to combat climate change', 10 August 2022. https://www.bbc.co.uk/news/uk-england-beds-bucks-herts-62486426.

along the river. On a hot day it was too tempting so we both paddled our feet, refreshed by the cool clear waters of the Ash.

The Amwell Walkway continues along the railway line; the footpath and cycleway links up with the Lee Valley Park. The river widens and grows finally, joining the river Lea above Stanstead Abbotts and not far from the popular bird sanctuary of the Amwell Nature Reserve. It's home to a huge variety of birds including bitterns and terns. Just along from this is the Amwell Magna Fishery, home to the former punk rock star, angler and now tireless river campaigner Feargal Sharkey. He is well placed to understand the conditions of our chalk streams.

In spite of the best efforts of the Herts and Middlesex Wildlife Trust, who have hosted the River Ash Catchment Partnership,[64] the Ash, as much as any river I walked in Hertfordshire, felt severely depleted. Much of this reflects over-abstraction for our high levels of domestic use and farming. More wetlands and rainwater capture are needed. These are issues beyond the ability of volunteer groups to address directly, but any river can benefit from having friends. Maybe a 'Friends of the Ash' group will emerge to champion the river, and join the coalition of others to review wider government policy and resourcing of regulatory bodies.

....

64 Herts and Middlesex Wildlife Trust, The River Ash – A Living Landscape, 2015. https://www. youtube.com/watch?v=S5ua0dP2ZSg.

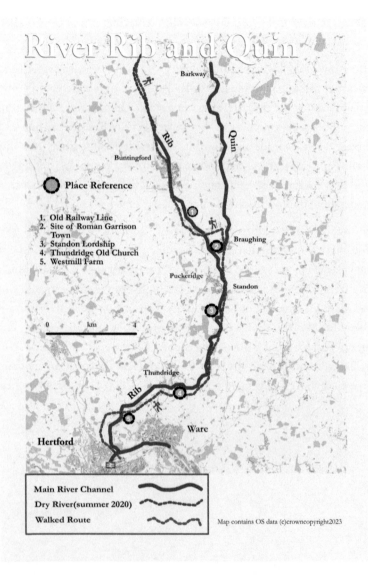

River Rib and Quin

Barkway

Rib

Quin

Buntingford

Place Reference

1. Old Railway Line
2. Site of Roman Garrison Town
3. Standon Lordship
4. Thundridge Old Church
5. Westmill Farm

Braughing

Puckeridge

Standon

0   km   4

Thundridge

Rib

Ware

Hertford

Main River Channel	
Dry River(summer 2020)	
Walked Route	

Map contains OS data (c)crowncopyright2023

Route Map for Rib and Quin

13. The Rib and the Quin – quiet rivers in need of a boost

Taking public transport to get to my walks was the best option all round (healthier and no need to return to a parked car), but it could be a challenge. Not least to reach the remote source of the Rib high up in the hills of North Hertfordshire. I took trains from Hertford up to Royston, then walked back. It was certainly the long way around, over 40km. From Royston I followed the Icknield Way Trail, passing Therfield Heath where long and bell barrows mark some of the county's earliest settlements from the Neolithic and Bronze Ages (4000–2000 BC).

Not far from Therfield I reached the location where maps indicated the source of the Rib. Not unexpectedly I found no spring waters. The river channel ran along a quiet lane through scattered homes at Dane End. Not the only 'Dane End' in Hertfordshire. This lane and the river was probably the frontier between Saxon Mercia and Danish Anglia back in the Middle Ages.

Further on I passed Therfield Sewage Plant. According to the Rivers Trust[65] this spilled 26 times into the river in 2021, a total of 243 hours. Can't be good, especially with such low flows. Finally, the Rib trickled then it flowed to Buckland and Buntingford. Several feasible paths are possible from Chipping for public use along the river edge (map 14). Locals had already made an informal path on the edge of one field in Buckland, understandably as the other choice was the fast-moving A10.

....
65   The Rivers Trust, *Raw Sewage in Our Rivers*. https://theriverstrust.org/key-issues/sewage-in-rivers?mc_cid=c6247f0b70&mc_eid=d713c1005c.

Map 14

Getting into Buntingford the Rib is quite hidden away. It runs east of the main high street through residential areas. Many sections are set in deep channels, squeezed by roads or the retaining walls of encroaching development (photo 21). It's how we did things for decades, but it's unsustainable drainage practice which only increases the flooding risk downstream. The County Bridge, built in 1937 according to a date stone, crosses the river Rib at the end of the high street, its substantial size reflecting both the former and potential river flow. In Chapel Lane a recently flooded house on the edge of the old town centre had the dehumidifiers running to dry the building out. Thames Water said this was a one in 99 years event. It's an area at risk.[66] Local people objected to the poor maintenance of gullies and drains. It wasn't the first time. Heavy rain has brought a lot of flooding in Buntingford, especially in 1968 when the river backed up from the bridge.

South of Buntingford I had to do a lot of road walking and I was thrown back onto the A10 verge for a while. Frustrating, because if public rights had been safeguarded on the old railway line below Buntingford when it was closed, this would probably provide one of the best walking and cycling routes in Hertfordshire. The idea must have occurred to others. It would give people walking or on bicycles especially a much safer route than heavily trafficked local roads (map 15). Where there's a will, there should still be a way. Using the old railway line between Buntingford and Braughing as a green travel corridor could act as a boost to local businesses, offering people safe and healthy recreation, and be extended to link with destinations such as Standon Farm.

21. Engineered river channel.

....
66   Environment Agency flood risk information, https://check-long-term-flood-risk.service.gov.
     uk/postcode.

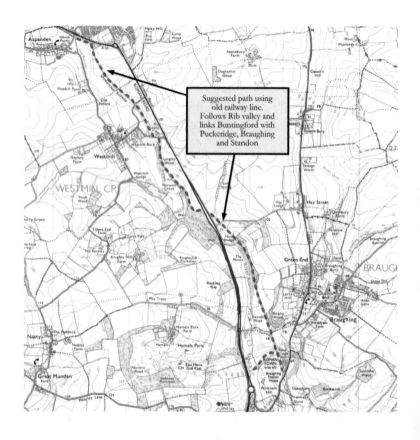

Map 15

Like other rivers in Hertfordshire the Rib is neither as large nor as long as it was historically. It is fed by its tributary the Quin, which flows down from the higher ground around Barkway. The Rib was once big enough for Romans to navigate all the way from the Lea and Ware. South of Braughing, the Romans built a garrison town at the junction of Ermine Street from London and Stane Street from Colchester. The location at the confluence of the Rib and the Quin was also one of an earlier

Iron Age settlement. The Roman town covered an area of 36 hectares laid out on a street grid of thatched timber houses, and included a bath house and possibly a Roman temple. Braughing reflects a pattern of post-Roman continuity of settlement in the area, although the Saxons placed themselves further up the valley where the Quin is forded. The ford by the central green is a picture-postcard scene in the centre of Braughing village, although I didn't get to see it being used as the route for village wheelbarrow races.

I took a right of way which had become established along the old railway line from Braughing Road to Standon and Puckeridge. The former Braughing railway station is in private ownership and can only be viewed from the main road. The Rib in Standon flows past a converted cornmill on the main A120, then runs between the backs of properties on the village high street and an industrial estate.

South of Standon, the river becomes accessible again and is probably one of the loveliest 'untouched' valleys of Hertfordshire. The branch railway came up the Ash rather than the Rib Valley, which may have helped. So, the river meanders its way down well away from large settlements and the sound of traffic. The valley is undulating and symmetrically sloped, amidst a rich mix of woodland, arable and grazing land. Unlike rivers such as the Mimram, it's quite publicly accessible as not many country houses were built here. One house of note is Standon Lordship. The Rib also has its fair share of fords and I stopped to admire one at Latchford (photo 22).

22. Latchford ford.

Another of my favourite resting points along the river is further down at Barwick Ford. From here you enter the hanging wood of Sawtrees, a Site of Special Scientific Interest and a beautiful stretch of ancient woodland. This led me to Cold Christmas Lane as there was no path along the river. Eventually a footpath took me down to the valley bottom below Cold Christmas. Here lie the ruins of a reputedly haunted fifteenth-century listed church tower at Thundridge. It's within the loop of the Rib where the earlier medieval village existed. Legend says the graves which lie in the abandoned graveyard belong mainly to young children and that one very frosty Christmas time, the village was hit by intense cold weather which led to their deaths. After this tragedy villagers decided to change the name of the village.

The tower is on the council's Heritage at Risk register. It's a Grade II* listed building and also a scheduled ancient monument. The Diocese of St Albans, who own it, have repeatedly expressed a wish to divest themselves of their interest, suggesting it might be sympathetically converted to residential use or if not then demolished. It raises that perennial question about whether you leave ruins to follow a natural path of decline, or repair and stabilise them as heritage frozen in time. I'm firmly in the latter camp, as are most of the public I suspect. For the Thundridge stump, it's a cost no public authority is willing, or able, to bear for decades. Signs warn you to keep back. A local group is campaigning to save the site.[67] Might it be worth trying crowdfunded commitments for its long-term repair, once a scheme is in place with the backing of public bodies? For the Rib Valley the tower is such a prominent local landmark and destination – one that would add value and interest to an enhanced green movement corridor.

I crossed the A10 at the village of Thundridge. Just up the hill on the main road is a monument to record a moment when Thomas Clarkson, on his way to London, decided he had to devote his life to the abolition of slavery. He did so for 61 years travelling over 35,000 miles on horseback. The listing describes his moving realisation and sense of calling.[68]

From Thundridge you naturally chose the valley paths towards the golf course at Hanbury Manor, now a pricey hotel but once a convent school. At Westmill Farm I would have loved a direct path along the Rib down to the Lea Valley where it joins the river at Kingsmeads. Instead, I had

....

67   Thundridge Old Church, https://thundridgeoldchurch.org
68   *'At Cambridge, in 1785, Clarkson wrote the winning Latin prize essay for which the set topic was 'Anne liceat invitos in servitutem dare' ('Is it lawful to enslave the unconsenting?'). Research into the Atlantic slave trade left him appalled, in June 1785, when he was riding from Cambridge to London to embark on his career, he dismounted on the hill above Wadesmill and 'sat down disconsolate on the turf by the roadside and held my horse. Here a thought came into my mind, that if the contents of the Essay were true, it was time some person should see these calamities to their end.' William Wordsworth's poem, 'To Thomas Clarkson' celebrates this moment when 'the constant Voice ...Which, out of thy young heart's oracular seat, / First roused thee.' And it is this moment, of pivotal importance for the history of the British abolition movement, that the Clarkson Monument commemorates'.* Historic England. Clarkson Monument on High Cross Hill. List description https://historicengland.org.uk/listing/the-list/list-entry/1281321?section=official-list-entry

to take lanes up to Chapmore End, crossing busy roads. A direct valley route looks perfectly feasible (map 16) and would connect neighbouring settlements, Thundridge with Hertford, and places en route such as Westmill Farm with its leisure activities and fishing lakes. It was quite a tough end to a marathon day's walking that finished in persistent rain. The kind of ending that makes you value the bare necessities of life: shelter in a dry home, warmth and something to eat.

A community group, Friends of the River Rib and Quin, aware that their rivers were suffering, was set up in 2019 and are lately getting their act together with a website,[69] events, detailed river surveys and river monitoring by trained volunteers. They challenge Affinity's abstraction and promote greater access to the river, estimating perhaps only 7% of it is currently accessible. Their presence and membership are growing fast, and that augurs well for the future.

---

69 Friends of the Rib and Quin, https://friendsoftherib.wordpress.com/.

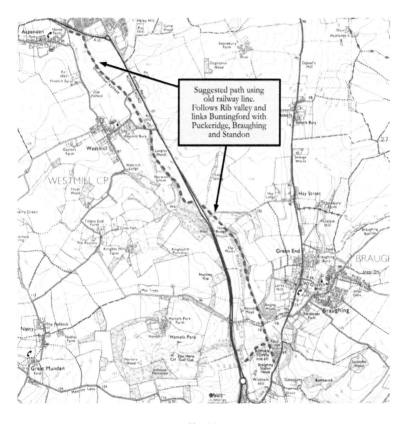

Suggested path using old railway line. Follows Rib valley and links Buntingford with Puckeridge, Braughing and Standon

Map 16

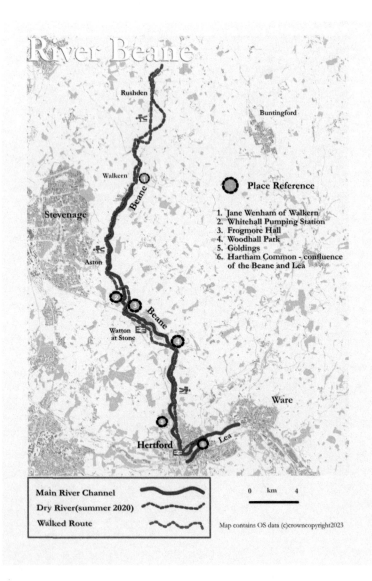

Route Map for Beane

14. The Beane – awaiting the return of its song

Up on the chalk plateau near Roe Green I hunted the source of the river Beane, taking buses from Hertford to Buckland and a trek across upland Hertfordshire. Well, the source was more of a 'has been', although as I learned later, in summer the spring wouldn't generally flow as the upper reach is a winterbourne.

I followed a dry ditch, enjoying the good clean air, distant views and a sparsely populated landscape. Wildflower strips at the edge of fields left by the farmer looked colourful and were appreciated as I walked along the first ditch (photo 23); these provide wildlife corridors and can be a buffer to harmful chemicals seeping into the soil and water.

23. Wildflower buffer strip.

It was then road walking for a couple of miles given the lack of a river path (Map 17). Pools of water within the riverbed of the Beane were found at Luffenhall. The hamlet straddles the administrative boundary of North and East Hertfordshire districts. The stream didn't get going until I reached the ford at Church End, Walkern. This is a place of local history as it's where Jane Wenham lived, one of the last people to be condemned to death as a witch in England (fortunately pardoned) – harking back to a time when rivers and ponds were used to punish and kill. In medieval times ducking was a test. If somebody could survive, they were a witch. If they didn't, they were innocent.

Map 17

The Beane runs to the rear of high street houses and passes a converted flour mill as it leaves Walkern. A modest stream was evident and that continues all the way to Watton at Stone with intermittent dry sections (photo 24). Historic and unsustainable abstraction is primarily to blame, as boreholes were added to supply water to the nearby post-war new town of Stevenage. In 2012, a local folk band, Blue Harbour, wrote a protest song (Fig.3) for the Beane with the lines:

And at Whitehall we cry for they're pumping it dry,
Yes, they're draining the old River Beane.[70]

24. Dry river, Whitehall.

70   Blue Harbour (Phil Hewett and Jim Coombes), 'On the Banks of the Beane', 2012.
     https://www.facebook.com/watch/?v=195066004964659.

Figure 3. Lyrics . *The Banks of the Beane*

By Blue Harbour (Phil Hewett and Jim Coombes)

On the banks of The Beane, George and I we go walking
The crystal clear water it makes our hearts sing
Where the swallows swoop low
George runs to and fro
Scaring pheasant and partridge away
Kingfishers and otters at play

But it's a dream for the river is gone
From Old Hall to Cromer we can't hear its song
And at Walkern the mill
It stands very still
As it grieves for the old River Beane.

On the banks of The Beane George and I we go walking,
Bright sun on the water,insects on the wing.
As I cast my line out
To a basking brown trout,
A heron looks on in disdain,...
As I hopefully cast out again.

But it's a dream for the river is gone
From Walkern to Aston we can't hear its song
And at White Hall we cry for they're pumping it dry
Yes, they're draining the old River Beane.

On the banks of The Beane George and I we go walking
Past broken old willows collapsed in despair
No swallows swoop low
As George runs to and fro
No pheasant or partridge to scare
For the wild life it just isn't there

But we still dream though the river is gone
From White Hall to Watton we can't hear its song
Then at Hertford we see where it joins with The Lee
All that's left of the old River Beane.

And the best we can tell
OFWAT say go to hell
Because it's cheap you can weep for your dream
Say farewell to the old River Beane

Words and melody copyright © 2012 Blue Harbour

Well, maybe it helped prompt Affinity Water's River Beane Catchment Management Plan, which began in 2014. Legislative changes in the 2014 Water Act were significant, as they enabled abstraction licences to be changed without compensation to water companies. The River Beane Restoration Association[71] was formed in 1991 and a long objective of theirs was to close the infamous Whitehall pumping stations[72] which I passed near the river below Aston. Public pressure over the last decade has now brought genuine reductions of 18 million litres a day and a commitment by Affinity to progressively end 'unsustainable abstraction'. That's a little vague on detail but it's progress.

The Beane moves through its wide gentle slopes down to Watton at Stone. It's great recreation for residents of Aston to wander out on high paths and admire the long valley views from the occasional public seat. On the higher ground to the east lies Benington – the 'settlement of the people of the Beane'. Westerly wind speeds pick up here and the upper fields were the scene of a long planning battle over proposed wind turbines. Two applications were dismissed after planning inquiries. They would have been highly visible, and liking them or not was subjective. I suspect in time they might have become an accepted part of the landscape – but how much better if local communities owned them and benefited directly from their cheap clean electricity.

To come off the uncomfortably fast Walkern Road, I took a permissive footpath through the parkland of Frogmore Hall crossing the Beane and the Stevenage Brook, which comes down from Stevenage town and joins here. The Beane Restoration Association have organised removal of highly invasive Himalayan balsam along here and on the brook. The balsam suffocates other plants and leaves banks bare in winter with greater siltation of the riverbed.

....
71 River Beane Restoration Association, https://www.riverbeane.org.uk/about-us/.
72 See the River Lea Catchment Partnership: https://www.riverleacatchment.org.uk/ and https://www.riverleacatchment.org.uk/index.php/river-beane-news-and-events/river-beane-news/1237-river-beane-catchment-partnership-meeting-minutes-01-dec-2022.

As a walker I'd much rather stay close to the river than follow roads, but I had to take the narrow pavement to the A602 which would be best avoided altogether. The Watton at Stone Neighbourhood Plan is promoting riverside access and wetlands for Rush Meads at the northern entrance to the village, and also includes a green corridor policy primarily for the Beane. That longer Beane Valley Path could be on its way (map 18).

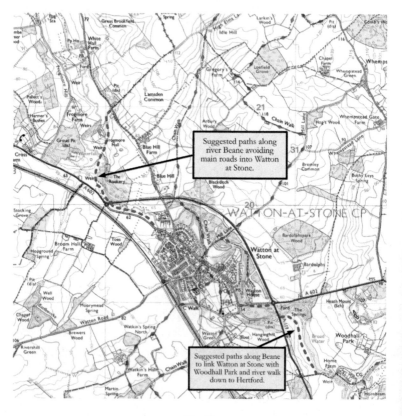

Map 18

East of the village the river Beane is fully accessible from The Lammas, an area of common land in the floodplain. At Mill Lane a neglected industrial building interrupts connection of the commons with the village. A gap is evident as no footpaths follow the river until it is rejoined south of Watton in Woodhall Park. This was originally the eighteenth-century country home built on the spectacularly rapid and ill-gotten gains of Thomas Rumbold – a 'nabob' or get-rich-quick officer in the East India Company. The estate has been sold on since and the house is now leased to Heath Mount School.

Whatever the season, it's always a beautiful walk through Woodhall Park, a landscaped area which created Broadwater Lake by damming the river Beane. Storm Katie in 2016 brought flash flooding, a surge and a breach of the lake. A three-year project of Woodhall estate with Affinity Water has restored the weir, diversified river channel habitats, and created new reed beds upstream and a new chalk stream around the lake to allow fish to swim upstream (photo 25). In summer 2022, 130 water voles were released by the Herts and Middlesex Wildlife Trust,[73] part of their goal of re-establishing water voles in the streams of Hertfordshire.

....
73 Herts and Middlesex Wildlife Trust, *Reintroducing Water Voles to the River Beane at the Woodhall Estate*, July 2022. https://www.youtube.com/watch?v=c5gCLkuzAWQ.

25. Woodhall Park.

The Beane from Woodhall Park down to Hertford is rightly one of the most popular river footpaths in Hertfordshire. I should know – living in Hertford, I've walked it countless times. It passes through the villages of Stapleford, with its distinctive church and tower on the river, and Waterford with meadows that flood regularly in winter. It's quite heavily wooded, and there are plans for selective felling to improve light penetration and diversity within the stream by the River Beane Catchment Partnership. Conservation grazing and river restoration is also planned for Waterford Marshes in an area well connected by paths, including an archway beneath the adjacent railway line.

Seeing somebody using a high-powered jet spray to wash a car, prompted several thoughts. It's convenient but I couldn't help but wonder at the copious amounts of good-quality drinking water. How much water is used to wash cars? There are 40 million registered vehicles in the UK. High consumption is part of the problem of water-deprived rivers, as I'd witnessed that day. You wonder where the leadership can be found, to challenge our attitudes. Water is a precious and finite resource. But there aren't many votes in saying 'limit your use'. Don't we tend to assume water is ours by right and will always be there whenever we please? The government directs planning authorities that they have to assume water will be provided for developments, whether that be in applications or plans that meet housing targets. Water companies are legally required to provide water, but our rivers don't have 'rights'. It's a question being asked around the world – and we could learn from an indigenous people's world view in examining our interconnectedness with nature.[74]

After a short road section on the A119 (a route via the Goldings entrance would be better), I followed the track alongside a dried-up mill race to a former mill site. The access road to this area is a quiet walk which connects seamlessly into the Port Hill area of Hertford. Nearby land to the north of Beane Road, an alarm was raised over the division and sale of land in lots, alongside the river. Although Green Belt land, there was great concern about fragmented speculative ownership and neglect. 'Save Beane Marshes' was set up and used crowdfunding to purchase the land to safeguard its future. Now it has been entrusted to the Herts and Middlesex Wildlife Trust and has seen active work including the reintroduction of grazing livestock. CPRE Hertfordshire granted the group an award in 2022 for 'Improving and protecting the environment', praising the enthusiastic local community effort.[75]

The Beane ultimately merges with the Lea at The Warren in Hartham Common, Hertford. The Environment Agency carried out some groundwork here in 2013, creating new ponds and wetlands with grazing regimes to promote biodiversity and wildflowers. Hartham's valley slopes frame the space around the Beane and the Lea with Bengeo at the top,

....

74 Patrick Barkham, 'Should rivers have the same rights as people?', *The Guardian*, 25 July 2021. https://www.theguardian.com/environment/2021/jul/25/rivers-around-the-world-rivers-are-gaining-the-same-legal-rights-as-people.

75 CPRE Hertfordshire Awards, https://www.cpreherts.org.uk/news/cpre-hertfordshire-awards-2022/.

the 'spur of land of the people of the river Beane'. Hartham Common in the valley is a popular destination – once a scene of battles and horse racing, it's a huge green public space and previously had its own bracing outdoor pool fed directly by the waters of the Beane.

Major challenges remain for the Beane. Water quality and quantity are both poor. It's just as well that there is a growing local campaign group for its restoration. Following the publication of the Chalk Stream Strategy in 2021,[76] the Beane was chosen as one of eight catchments across the country to host two pilot schemes with flagship restoration to tackle flow, quality and habitat in unison. This includes a citizen science monitoring initiative aimed at improving and standardising data collection. Both will simultaneously run in the Beane.

If we can see more coherent national policy and reduced abstraction, and if funds can be committed for physical restoration work such as in the River Lea Catchment Partnership, hopefully in time we shall hear the song of the Beane return.

---

76   Chalk Stream Restoration Group, *Chalk Stream Strategy* 2021, https://catchmentbasedapproach.org/learn/chalk-stream-strategy-3/.

River Mimram

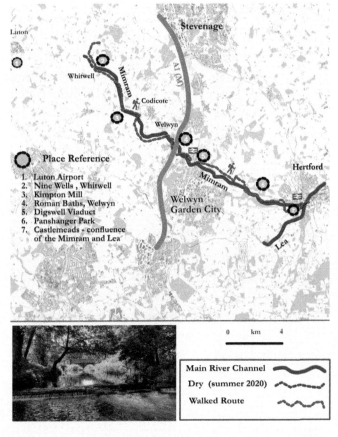

Luton

Stevenage

Whitwell

Mimram

A1 (M)

Codicote

Welwyn

Place Reference

1. Luton Airport
2. Nine Wells , Whitwell
3. Kimpton Mill
4. Roman Baths, Welwyn
5. Digswell Viaduct
6. Panshanger Park
7. Castlemeads - confluence
   of the Mimram and Lea

Mimram

Hertford

Welwyn
Garden City

Lea

0   km   4

Main River Channel	
Dry (summer 2020)	
Walked Route	

Route Map for Mimram

15. The Mimram – a rather private delight

Hertfordshire is a 'home county' long influenced by the reach of London's economy and society. No river reveals this more than the Mimram, one of her most delightful chalk stream valleys. Its attractiveness and proximity to London, Hertford, Hatfield House and St Albans made it popular as a rural retreat for the wealthy. Government officials, royal courtiers, traders and merchants built a series of grand country residences in the valley over the centuries. The houses were a 'canvas' for the work of eighteenth century landscape designers as a fashion grew for the natural 'picturesque'.[77] These parklands would remove all signs of human habitation including public roads, paths and peasants, restoring the land to a mythical undisturbed idyll. A statement of power and status for the owner, it was also a landscape of seclusion and exclusion.

Taking the train to reach the head of the river meant a long walk from Stevenage. The din of A1(M) traffic receded as I walked west. I rounded the house of Stagenhoe, sat down and found myself directly beneath the path of planes taking off from Luton Airport. There were fewer than usual in 2020 due to the pandemic, but their periodic thunderous roar as they climbed steeply was markedly at odds with the area's rural tranquillity. Even in a climate emergency, Luton Airport is being proposed for huge expansion. Many of us love the countryside and love to travel. Flying from Luton, as elsewhere, it's too easy to forget the impact on the ground below, or the impact on the planet. It's not unlike how when travelling in a car we forget our impact on people and the world outside.

I eventually reached the mooted source of the river Mimram. Within a bed of reeds west of Whitwell, this was private land and there was no

77   Carl Thompson, 'The picturesque at home and abroad', British Library. https://www.bl.uk/picturing-places/articles/the-picturesque-at-home-and-abroad.

visible water to be seen. Just off Lilley Bottom Lane I caught up with a small puddle at a ford to the river channel. Reaching Whitwell, the stream had got going a little. Here, until recently, was Nine Wells, one of the rare surviving watercress businesses in Hertfordshire (photo 26). Now I could see and enjoy the flow of the famed 'gin clear' waters passing a wide area of watercress beds. Staying close to the water down the valley wasn't possible (additional paths are suggested - maps 19 and 20) and I had to walk along the Codicote Road, which didn't feel comfortable for a lone pedestrian. As I reached Kimpton Mill, an off-road route became available by Rye End Cottages along the river down to Codicote Bottom. A refreshing change.

26. Watercress Farm.

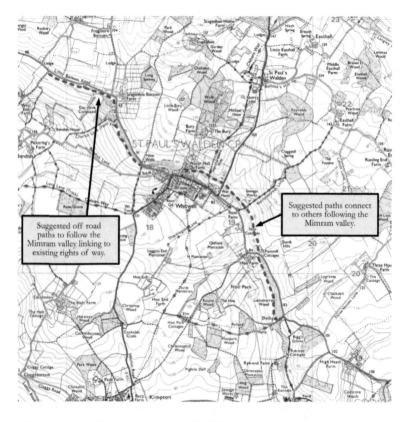

Map 19

Wandering Kimpton Road, a quiet lane to Welwyn, I couldn't help noticing rubbish and plastic strewn along highway verges and in hedges. It may have been thrown from passing vehicles. Walking makes you notice the rubbish more, not least all the plastic plants, artificial lawns and even plastic fences. The day after my walk I heard of the high levels of microplastics that researchers have found in the river Thames. It's not enough to focus on individual behaviour. Apparently, a truckload of plastic refuse is dumped in the ocean every minute. We can't go on like this. A huge shift in attitudes but also policy and regulation is needed to design an economy that is not based on producing and throwing away plastic. Plastic inevitably breaks down into the environment and our rivers, and then enters our drinking water and the food chain. We are not separate from nature and the environment, just as we can't separate ourselves from the consequences of our actions.

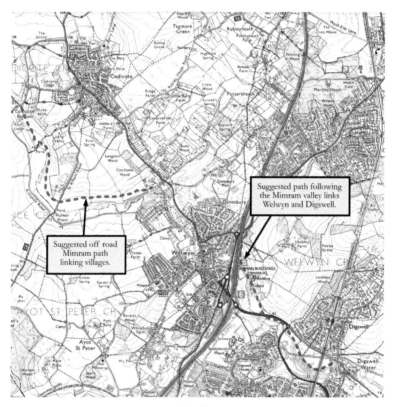

Map 20

The Mimram can also be accessed through the local nature reserve of Singlers Marsh, on the north-west edge of Welwyn. Welwyn village was settled by the Romans as their road forded the river Mimram. In 1876 a young Vincent Van Gogh completed a 100 mile walk from Ramsgate to visit his sister in Welwyn. His route isn't known but he would possibly have enjoyed the walk up the Lea and Mimram valleys.[78]

The most accessible place to view the stream is a short-stay car park in the village centre. I couldn't help thinking how much more beneficial and inviting this would be as a green space. A community park for meeting that lets children play in the river. It's a question of priorities.

The Friends of the Mimram[79] have been campaigning to replenish river water levels and undertaking active projects for the stream as part of the River Lea Catchment Partnership.[80] Two notable successes have been the agreements to revoke groundwater abstraction licences at Fulling Mill Pumping Station and for significant reductions at Digswell. The combined impacts should see about 18 million litres a day retained for the aquifer. The campaign continues; the website notes the decline in brown trout and fish populations over the years.

From Welwyn, the Mimram goes under the A1(M). Archaeological works had long been excavating the site of some Roman Baths here, but in spite of this the Ministry of Transport proposed and proceeded to build the motorway over the top of them. The remains of this Scheduled Ancient Monument can be visited by the public in its steel vault, deep beneath Junction 6 of the A1 (M). The river skirts the Lockleys estate (now Sherrardswood School) going towards Digswell. Forming part of the landscape park of Digswell House, the Mimram flows past the

....

78 Van Gogh Museum. The letters. No 84 To Theo Van Gogh. Welwyn, Saturday, 17 June 1876. https://www.vangoghletters.org/vg/letters/let084/letter.html#translation

79 Friends of the Mimram Facebook page: https://www.facebook.com/profile. php?id=100067114943023.

80 River Lea Catchment Partnership, https://www.riverleacatchment.org.uk/index.php/river-mimram-home.

spring-fed landscape feature of Digswell Lake constructed in 1810, which outflows over a weir into the Mimram. In Digswell the Mimram can also be accessed from the playing field east of the viaduct before it runs through the grounds of the Mill House, the location of a historic watermill.

Nine country houses were built along the Mimram Valley, including Panshanger and Tewin Water, remodelled by Humphry Repton and Lancelot 'Capability' Brown who also worked on Cole Green and Digswell House. The parkland of Digswell has become somewhat lost amidst the northern expansion of Welwyn Garden City and associated busy roads.

In 1850 the valley changed dramatically with the construction of the Digswell Railway Viaduct. It is 100 foot high with forty arches modelled on a Roman aqueduct. The viaduct was needed for the main East Coast railway line and any route up the river valley had been resisted by wealthy landowners. Opened by Queen Victoria she was too scared of its height to take the train across it.[81] It's a magnificent example of industrial architecture; a Grade II* listed structure. Construction required 13 million bricks, the blue skin being added later over original red bricks. The lane under the viaduct was closed during the Covid pandemic. With 88% local support this was made permanent to provide safe walking and cycling – it works perfectly as part of the Centenary Circular Walk of Welwyn Garden City. I broke for afternoon tea with friends who lived nearby and they then joined me to walk the valley along to Panshanger.

Welwyn Garden City lies south of the Mimram. It was founded in 1920 on land from the Panshanger and Digswell estates purchased by Ebenezer Howard. It was developed on higher ground between the Mimram and the Lea, so wasn't centred on a river as such. Its water supplies were an issue from the beginning, as the Lea Conservancy Act meant it couldn't

....
81   See Tony Rook's book. *River Mimram*. Amberley Publishing, 2014.

discharge sewage into either the Mimram or Lea. Its idealistic vision of Town and Country remains a potent one for many, but one that arguably has drifted into a more standard suburbia. Boreholes were sunk to meet the city's water demands but have depleted the Mimram.

Unfortunately, not much of the Mimram is accessible through the Tewin Water estate, but Liz and Paul showed me the path to a small footbridge over the river where an artificial but naturalistic stone weir has clear water tumbling over it. This was part of the designed landscape garden of Tewin Water House. Beyond this was Tewinbury Farm where the stream bubbles healthily and clear across a gravel bed and under an old bridge. It's been made a feature of this popular hospitality and wedding venue, with a permissive path along the stream. This provides good public access and a great setting for wedding photos.

27. Poplar Green, nr Panshanger.

Circling Archers Green the path came back to a bridge and weir at Poplars Green (photo 27). With the water's gentle flow, trailing plants and green grass in the shade of a tree, the scene was a quintessential chalk stream resting space. It has long been a popular informal site known locally to families on picnics, but without management and due to problems of on-road parking it was closed off. It would make a superb link within a Mimram Valley route heading into Panshanger Park (map 21). Hopefully the Herts and Middlesex Wildlife Trust will be successful in their quest to purchase the site.[82]

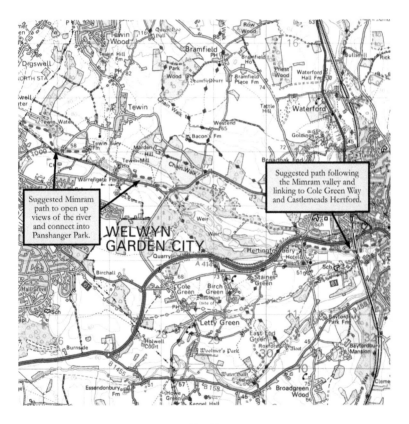

Map 21

....
82   See Archers Green Appeal. Hertfordshire and Middlesex Wildlife Trust
     https://www.hertswildlifetrust.org.uk/archersgreen

The former gravel extracted landscapes of Panshanger Park provide the largest public area along the Mimram, fulfilling the conditions of a 1980 planning permission. It can now be enjoyed by all, though was once the private privilege of Earl Cowper's country home and Hertford's high-society gatherings. The main house was demolished in the 1950s. Over the last decade a Friends of Panshanger Park[83] group has set out a vision and worked with urgency to get it open. The ruins of a listed orangery to the house survive, and await ideas and funds to bring it into use. After decades of sand and gravel extraction, the Repton-inspired landscape has been restored with large fishing lakes stocked with trout and popular for waterfowl. A platform on the island in the middle of the Osprey Lake has been visited by migrating ospreys on their way to Africa. Many lakeside areas are accessible to the public. Longhorn cattle have been brought in to graze. Weekly park runs take place. There are about 800 veteran trees in the park, including the renowned Panshanger Oak – reputedly the largest 'clear-stemmed' (not pollarded) oak in the country. Planted in the second half of the sixteenth century, possibly by Queen Elizabeth I, it has been visited by Queen Victoria, Queen Elizabeth II and Winston Churchill. Today the oak measures 25 feet (7.6 metres) round its girth. Public access can bring some problems. Dog owners are asked to keep their pets out of the stream near areas safeguarded for water vole, as toxic flea sprays used on pet dogs can pollute and damage aquatic life.[84]

I left by a path under the A414 along the Mimram. It leads straight to the village of Hertingfordbury. The main village road crosses the stream and Hertingfordbury mill race, and the mill has been converted to apartments. The Mimram is out of public view again as it flows into the

....

83   Friends of Panshanger Park, https://friendsofpanshangerpark.co.uk/.
84   'Potential role of veterinary flea products in widespread pesticide contamination of English rivers', *Science of The Total Environment*, Volume 755, Part 1, 10 February 2021. https://doi.org/10.1016/j.scitotenv.2020.143560.

Fermin Koop, 'We're using flea treatments on our pets and it's polluting rivers and streams', ZME Science, 20 November 2020. https://www.zmescience.com/science/were-using-flea-treatments-on-our-pets-and-its-polluting-rivers-and-streams/.

grounds of Epcombs and Hertingfordbury Park where an eighteenth-century spring-fed canal runs 140 metres down to the river. The Mimram flows along the backs of housing in Hertford with occasional access points. After the railway viaduct it finally joins the River Lea at Castlemeads to the west of Hertford, another area that has been noted for a small colony of water vole.

Given the protected views of private owners along the Mimram river, it is difficult to imagine a Mimram Valley Path being agreed voluntarily along its full length, but I feel the ambition should be there. I have set out several possible links (maps 19-21) to enable this for the fuller enjoyment of the river. This also addresses safety issues given the lack of off-road options for walking. At its best, the Mimram and its valley is a jewel in the Hertfordshire countryside and it deserves to be fully enjoyed by all.

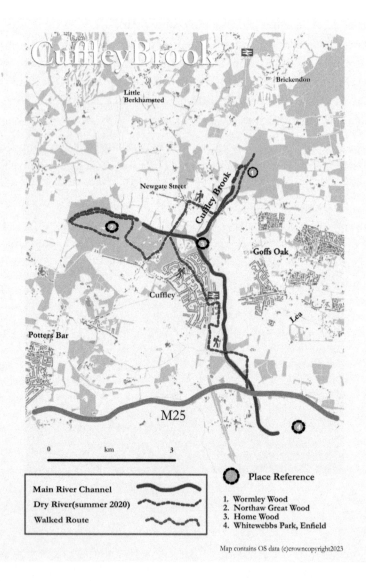

Route Map for Cuffley Brook

16. Cuffley Brook – a little local discovery

As part of my 'whole Hertfordshire' experience, I walked to discover a small river that I'd not heard of before. The Cuffley Brook runs close to the southern edge of the county and is a tributary of the river Lea. It meets with Turkey Brook outside Hertfordshire and merges with the Lea in Greater London near to the lock at Enfield village.

The brook's sources are several and found within a swathe of ancient woodland in southern Hertfordshire. Here coppiced areas have long provided a source of fuel locally and for export to London. I noted how these woodlands come into their own in the heat of summer with their own microclimate. Walking them on a hot day was comfortably magnificent.

I took the train from Hertford to Bayford then walked to Wormley Wood, part of the Broxbourne Woods National Nature Reserve. Maps suggested it was a source for Cuffley Brook; certainly it's a tributary. The wood is a mix of mainly oak and hornbeam, managed by the Woodland Trust and a haven for wildlife. On its east side there are feeder channels to the Wormleybury Brook which flows directly east to the river Lea. Up here I found low water levels in ponds that feed watercourses flowing south toward Cuffley. I couldn't follow the river until I caught up with the Cuffley Brook as it passed beneath the Newgate Street village road bridge. There was a flow of water and some gentle gurgling sounds to enjoy but the river didn't honestly look too healthy.

I watched the water go on its way, then proceeded to find the likely main source of the Cuffley Brook from ponded areas up in the 300-acre Northaw Great Wood Country Park. When I got there the pond held some water (photo 28) but there was nothing in the dry channels that will at times fill and feed into the brook. Northaw is a Site of Special

Scientific Interest. For centuries it provided open wood pasture with common grazing rights, as well as the pollarding of hornbeam for fuel. As income from grazing declined local lords pushed for its enclosure. Land enclosure profoundly influenced the English and Hertfordshire countryside as we know it, but over many centuries it brought great hardship, protests, acts of resistance such as 'hedge breaking', livestock trespass and violent repression by landowners. Enclosure fed the social divisions underlying the seventeenth-century English Civil War. Later the process was formalised by Acts of Parliament, which favoured property-owning MPs (who ruled Parliament). It peaked in the late eighteenth and early nineteenth centuries. Commoners were left landless, driven from agriculture and into the workshops of the Industrial Revolution.

28. Northaw Country Park.

In 1806 the Common of Northaw was enclosed by Act of Parliament, and from then until 1938 it was laid out and exploited as a more intense woodland for commercial timber production. Hertfordshire County

Council subsequently acquired the site and permitted public access. It was closed in World War II as part of the Outer London Stop Line, comprising a ring of anti-tank defences and pillboxes circling London. The local Home Guard, 'Dad's Army', exercised in Northaw. Their wartime map shows they renamed the Cuffley Brook the river Somme.

Northaw Wood is now managed by Welwyn Hatfield Borough Council and volunteers from the Friends of Northaw Great Wood.[85] In the sense that 'commoners' once again have access and enjoyment here, if not livelihood, it feels the wood has come full circle. There are swallow holes in the wood for subterranean water flow and many walking trails mostly circling from the main car park off the Ridgeway. I followed the line of the Cuffley Brook under the high sweeping tree cover of Northaw but the brook itself was dry. The north-east corner is fenced off from the wood. The Cuffley Active Learning Centre provides outdoor learning for schools and young groups. It would be a benefit to have a direct path close to the brook through this area (map 22) – this could link to Home Wood and the 'Hertfordshire Way' as a more convenient off-road walking route between Northaw Park and Cuffley.

85   Friends of Northaw Great Wood, http://www.fongw.org.uk/.

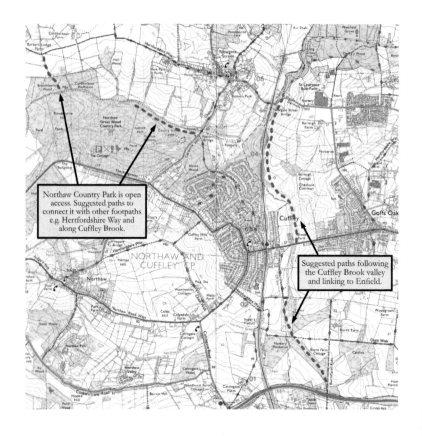

Northaw Country Park is open access. Suggested paths to connect it with other footpaths e.g. Hertfordshire Way and along Cuffley Brook.

Suggested paths following the Cuffley Brook valley and linking to Enfield.

Map 22

I followed the Hertfordshire Way through the suburbs of Cuffley. There is no path along the valley bottom of the brook which runs beneath an otherwise impenetrable railway embankment. I passed the railway station, and went down Cuffley Hill to find the point where the main road crosses the river to the east of the village. Though I anticipated more water at this lower point, in fact there was less than I'd seen before.

Further along I came across a few pools with green algae. I guessed this reveals the impact of water abstraction on groundwater levels and the local consumption of water for Cuffley. It's a brook rather than a main river but the channels it runs in, the lack of water and lack of public access mean Cuffley Brook doesn't offer the habitat or enjoyment that it might for the good residents of Cuffley. I walked down to the county boundary where the river goes under the M25, new paths along the river would be possible here (map 22). Beyond Hertfordshire it feeds lakes in Whitewebbs Park in Enfield, then joins Turkey Brook and finally runs down to the river Lea.

Many people probably never get to see Cuffley Brook. This account may not have encouraged them to do so, but then it's a vicious circle. Out of sight, out of mind? The Northaw and Cuffley Neighbourhood Plan 2023[86] includes provision of new green walking routes where they would improve access to the parish's green infrastructure network. The brook deserves to be brought more fully into public view as part of this network, and some further connecting paths will greatly help.

....
86 'Policy D3: Green Infrastructure', *Northaw and Cuffley Neighbourhood Plan March* 2023. https://northawcuffleypc.org.uk/the-neighbourhood-plan/.

River Lea

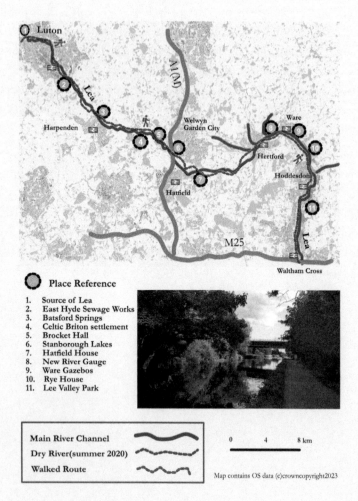

Place Reference

1. Source of Lea
2. East Hyde Sewage Works
3. Batsford Springs
4. Celtic Briton settlement
5. Brocket Hall
6. Stanborough Lakes
7. Hatfield House
8. New River Gauge
9. Ware Gazebos
10. Rye House
11. Lee Valley Park

Main River Channel	
Dry River(summer 2020)	
Walked Route	

0   4   8 km

Map contains OS data (c)crowncopyright2023

Route Map for Lea

17. The Lea –
a walk across Hertfordshire

The Lea provides the longest river route through Hertfordshire. There is a designated Lea Valley Walk, 53 miles long from Luton down to the Thames. It's not (yet) a national trail[87], but I think it should be and it would work well as a three- or four-day journey. I completed the Hertfordshire section of the Lea in two days. Firstly, from Hertford south down the Lea Valley and then, saving my legs for the last and longest day of this grand county tour, a 27-mile walk from the upper Lea at Luton, Bedfordshire, back to Hertford.

Its promotion as a trail is possibly frustrated by the fact that it cuts across a number of administrative boundaries – although, to paraphrase the singer Adele, you can't 'blame that on the River Lea'. At least the Lee Valley Regional Park[88] plays a good co-ordinating role from Ware down to the Thames. The Lea Catchment Partnership is also co-ordinating the work of river restoration.[89]

I went to find the source of the river at Leagrave in Luton. In the Victorian era, Leagrave was a popular holiday resort, referred to as Leagrave-on-Sea. The well head is within an area of interlocking springs and ponds (photo 29). Information boards explained that the name Lea may derive from a Celtic word 'Lug' meaning 'bright water' – a description that works for all good chalk streams. The springs not surprisingly have a long prehistory of settlement. Waulud's Bank and Ditch is an ancient monument that surrounds the source, possibly a Neolithic henge. From here water flows within a mostly walkable green

---

87 Natural England , *National Trails*. https://www.nationaltrail.co.uk/en_GB/trails/
88 The river is spelled 'Lee' or 'Lea'. By convention it is generally the 'Lea' upstream of Hertford and 'Lee' when referring to the Lee Navigation and Lee Valley Park, although 'Lea' is used regularly elsewhere within the lower Lea Valley!
89 The Lea Catchment Partnership, https://www.riverleacatchment.org.uk/.

finger through Luton's northern suburbs, before opening out at a lake in Wardown Park. I stayed the night at the Leaside Hotel from where I would walk to Hertford.

29. Source of the Lea.

Through Luton town centre, you lose sight of the Lea because it's been buried in subterranean culverts by post-war development, as many towns and cities did unthinkingly in the name of 'progress'. The Lea Partnership hopes to reopen these culverts, and long-anticipated plans for a new Luton Town football stadium at Power Court provide an opportunity. If it happens the river should again become a feature of the town centre. One landscape design objective for the development is to 'Integrate a well-defined green corridor along the river Lea ... to allow for education, biodiversity, recreation and play'. Let's hope it appears as the naturalised riverside area that the computer-generated images promote.

Blue signs to the 'Upper Lea Valley Way' guided me out of Luton and Bedfordshire into Hertfordshire. I was on a well-used metalled track, part of the Sustrans National Cycleway Network Route 6 which runs down to Harpenden. It's on the opposite side of the valley to the Lee Ho estate. There were cyclists, a few walkers, plenty of joggers and an artist's depiction of that much-loved comedian Eric Morecambe, famously a fan of Luton Town FC. The path passes the town's large sewage works at East Hyde (photo 30), whose treated outflows reputedly provide almost all the river Lea flow. Luton is a large town close to the river source. So, the Lea is not short of water but its quality is poor and dependent on how well these treatment works operate. From a bridge below the East Hyde outfall, I noted quite cloudy water and furry growth on the riverbed. The Rivers Trust website records that in 2022 the sewer storm overflow spilled four times for a total of just four hours [90] If you trust the figures, and some campaigners feel the EA aren't detecting all spills, that's a lot better than some sites.

30. East Hyde Treatment Works.

---

90   The Rivers Trust. Updated sewage map. https://theriverstrust.org/key-issues/sewage-in-rivers

The path uses the line of the former railway between Luton and Hatfield. This was closed in 1965, just when it might have become useful for package holiday flights then getting going from Luton Airport. I'd been this way before in early summer when the wide arable fields above Harpenden become a spectacle of bright red poppies. In Harpenden the footway was a bit narrow and overgrown – not sure how maintenance fits in with the local authority's five-year Greenspace Action Plan.[91] I took a break at Batsford Springs where boreholes were sunk in the past to boost water supplies for its watercress farming. Now it's a local nature reserve where I successfully managed the challenge of crossing the river using stepping stones; a safety ring was there for backup (photo 31).

31. Batsford Springs.

....
91 Greenspace Action Plans – Upper Lee Harpenden (https://www.stalbans.gov.uk/greenspace-action-plans) and Ayot Greenway (https://www.hertfordshire.gov.uk/media-library/documents/environment-and-planning/cms/plans-archive/ayot-greenway-gap-2020-25-final.pdf)

Wheathampstead village offers good river access and excellent walking. A post in the river records that I was 13 miles from Leagrave and 29 miles from the Thames. A plaque commemorates the event of a circus elephant drinking here and damaging the quay back in the 1940s. East of Wheathampstead are earthwork banks and ditches marking and defending the capital of the Catuvellauni tribe by the river Lea. The settlement was potentially the last place for Celtic Britons to resist Caesar in 54 BC.

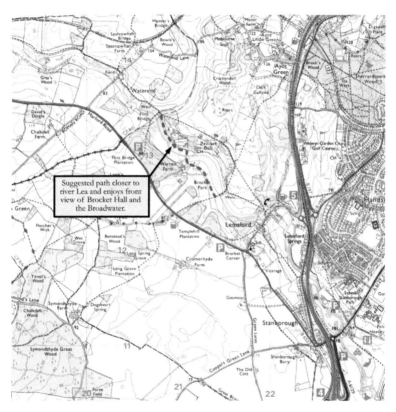

Map 23

The Lea path continues into more undulating, mixed woodland with arable fields. The river and trailing plants looked clean and clear at Waters End. From here the path headed up to the rear of Brocket Hall, now a golf course. The public path isn't best placed to enjoy views of the mansion and man-made lake fashioned from the Lea (map 23). The river Lea waters are fully in view again at the converted watermill, Lemsford Mill. Lemsford Springs are a wetland nature reserve.

If water levels aren't too high, you can take the Lea Valley Walk under the A1 motorway. Low headroom meant I had to duck. From here the river feeds the Stanborough Lakes, created as gravel was extracted for the construction of the A1. It is now a publicly owned park for boating, fishing and open-water swimming. A swimming lido, unheated and fed by the waters of the river Lea, opened in the 1930s but closed in 1999, leaving Welwyn Garden City without a main public swimming pool.

The river passed beneath the Great Northern railway line but I had to watch it go into private land. We reconnected at Mill Green by the A414. From here a new path for the Lea Valley Walk through Hatfield Park by the river would be excellent both for its history and to escape road traffic. Alternative paths are also needed to avoid hazardous walking along the B158 Lower Hatfield Road (map 24).

Map 24

It was getting dark as I came into the grounds of Hertford Castle, located by the river Lea for defence with an added moat. Hertford is the only place in the county where four rivers meet: the Lea, the Beane, the Mimram and the Rib. The star-like form of the town is heavily influenced by this fact as these green river fingers arrive from different directions. In the 1990s Hertford Civic Society commissioned a sculpture by William Pye, called 'Confluence' and positioned it in the main town square, to mark the fact. Unfortunately, like some of our chalk streams, the fountain tends to remain dry partly due to maintenance and running costs, and a lack of respect from some of the town's night visitors.

Hertford was settled at a ford on the river (where the Hart forded) and in Saxon times it provided a natural point of defence to establish two burghs marking the boundary with Danelaw territory to the north and east. From the Norman conquest Hertford became the administrative centre of the new county and enjoyed its royal connections. Queen Elizabeth I stayed at Hertford Castle and brought Parliament and Court there to escape the London plague.

The Lea was loud and furious at the weir by Hertford Theatre. Gradually the town is turning around to make more of its river frontages where the Lea cuts through a tightly built-up central area. The head of the navigation is by Folly Island in the centre of town. Boats can travel up to Hertford from London but must then turn back. The canal basin is enclosed by a footbridge across a long weir and is a superb entry point into Hartham Common. The footbridge here is also a popular spot to watch and photograph a resident kingfisher.

Hartham Common on the Lea is the town's premier recreational destination, ever more valued after the experience of the pandemic. After the outdoor pool closed, an outdoor lido followed which later became enclosed in a modern leisure centre. The common is a venue for football matches, tennis, children's play, climbing walls and running circuits. A five-year plan includes new otter habitats. The placing of otter holts and other efforts have been encouraging their return on the upper Lea for a number of years, but sightings are still all too rare.

After Hertford the lower half of the river Lea down to the M25 moves into a more densely populated region and probably some of the most heavily walked riverside paths in Hertfordshire. It's also my own back yard. I recall the remarkable scenes during the pandemic when literally hundreds of people, an inexhaustible line of walkers, stretched along the river towpath between Hertford and Ware for exercise and fresh air. Even in more normal times, on a sunny weekend the path between these river Lea towns gets busy with runners, cyclists or families taking a stroll.

The New River is neither new nor a river. It was built four centuries ago (1608–13) drawn from ancient holy springs at Chadwell to provide a rapidly growing London with safe and plentiful drinking water. It worked and still does. The New River Gauge was built later on to draw more water directly from the Lea just east of Hertford, now with a screen to prevent young elvers getting lost on their river journey. In 2020, the New River was supplying around 220 million litres of water per day, about 8% of London's total use.

Hertford and Ware both owe their location to crossing points on the river Lea, but their relative proximity has been a cause of occasionally violent rivalry between the towns. Roman Ermine Street ran from London to York fording the Lea at Ware but, after the loss of the bridge, Hertford became the most fordable point above London where the twin burghs were established. Later in 1191 Hertford rulers, in a dispute about bridge tolls, destroyed a new bridge at Ware[92] and then tried to block another but lost their monopoly of passage. It was then Ware which prospered by its position on the northern coaching route. It also had better river access, making it the pre-eminent malting town in Hertfordshire and England. Breweries and the malting business were well located to receive barley crops and the Lea was navigable to Ware from London and the sea, far earlier than Hertford.

Ware's collection of riverside summer houses is considered the best in the country. – these gazebos were refurbished in the 1980s. Built by wealthy high street inn owners for respite, they came to suffer from the industrial and domestic waste tipped into the river which left the

92   S. Williams, 'Ware's Bridge: a brief history', Hertfordshire's Community Archive Network, 2021. https://www.ourhertfordandware.org.uk/content/places/ware-places/transport-travel/ware_bridge.

Lea 'foul fetid and rank'. In 1864 the Inspector of Nuisances observed a 'black oily scum all over the river by the bridge which was fermenting with bubbles of gas and seething putrid mud by the banks'. In 1885, a music hall singer sang about poisoning his wife with the Lea's water.[93] It adds perspective to current-day pollution concerns.

I had to walk via the high street rather than take the towpath, as a footbridge was closed for six months awaiting replacement. Should essential walking infrastructure take six months to replace? Would it if pedestrians were truly at the top of the movement hierarchy? Ware marks the start of the Lee Valley Park. The organisation has provided strategic leadership to leisure and conservation since its establishment in 1967, regenerating the valley as a 'great playground for Londoners'. This is surely confirmed by one of the key attractions: the bird habitats at the Amwell Nature Reserve. I've done my share of bittern watching in the reeds.

At Stanstead Abbotts the riverside has wide green verges for people to enjoy the river and a drink at the Jolly Fisherman. There's a boat builder's and marina opposite. Stanstead St Margaret's has historically been vulnerable to flooding as it lies below the juncture of the Lea and the Stort, capturing waters from a wide catchment. The Lea lost its wetland marshes and meanders over the centuries as it was 'improved' for navigation and agriculture. Flood risks subsided after alleviation and flood relief channels were built in the 1970s, although several properties were flooded in the winter of 2013/14. The Environment Agency has identified properties that may be eligible for Property Flood Resilience (PFR) with specific provisions to limit the individual impact and upheaval of floods such as barriers, non-return valves to prevent backflow, wall sealants and the closing of airbricks.[94]

....
93 Ibid.
94 Environment Agency, 'Stanstead Abbotts Drain Information Page'. https://consult. environment-agency.gov.uk/hnl/stanstead-abbotts/.

Rye Meads, once an area of watercress beds, was developed as a major sewage treatment works to meet the demands of new towns at Harlow, Stevenage and Hatfield. When northern lagoons were no longer needed, they were offered to the RSPB. The area now has national and international designations as a Site of Special Scientific Interest (SSSI), a Special Protection Area (SPA) and a Wetland of International Importance under the 'Ramsar Convention'. Look out for the kingfisher, snipe, green sandpiper, shoveler, gadwall and tufted duck (a peregrine falcon was perched high on nearby pylons on one visit). Close by at Rye House, the riverside is subjected to the roar of go-karting, from a track where the Formula One champion Lewis Hamilton honed his early driving skills.

The Lee Valley Park is a mostly wetland area of recreational spaces and wildlife amidst retained horticulture and industry. The first main movement corridor between Hertfordshire and London, it got going with the river Lea, a key transport artery taking corn, barley and malt to the city and carrying goods and city 'nightsoil' out. By the 1930s the largest greenhouse industry in Britain was in the Lea Valley as market gardeners made use of its fertile soils, water and proximity to London markets. Some have been abandoned or redeveloped while many glasshouses still remain. The river is more or less straight with locks and weirs as it became canalised for increasingly large vessels.

Walking the towpath, it is evident how the numbers of people living on riverboats has grown – not only because of the attractiveness of a quieter, slower pace of life but also the impossibly inflated price of housing in the London area. The houseboats add to the scene and give the river a lived-in quality, so why not?

I eventually reached Waltham Cross where the London 2012 Olympic water sports centre was built and is retained as a legacy benefit. The river Lea marks the boundary of Hertfordshire with Essex from Rye Meads down to the M25. It was under an evening light that I stopped here at Hertfordshire's border (photo 32). The Lea flows on to north London, passes the Olympic site at Stratford, before exiting to the Thames and the North Sea. Most of the rain that falls in Hertfordshire leaves the county at this point. Who would have known?

32. The Lea leaves Hertfordshire.

18. My water use challenge … and a 'doughnut tariff' proposal

Before the walk I thought I was already pretty careful with water. I had eco-shower heads, didn't run the tap while brushing my teeth (24 litres a day!) and only did full washing loads etc. But witnessing many depleted local rivers, I became much more motivated to see what else I could do. Demand reduction matters in water-stressed areas such as Hertfordshire, as noted by the Chilterns Chalk Stream project:

The Chilterns area has some of the highest per capita demand for domestic water in the UK and environmentally unsustainable abstraction has persisted in some areas of the Chilterns for over 50 years, 173 litres of water per person per day compared to a national average of 142 litres of water per person per day.[95]

A personal effort

Just checking the estimated amounts used for different home activities helped. Eighteen litres for a shower. Six litres to flush. I noticed I often ran a tap waiting for the water to run hot, losing a few litres each

....
95 'Celebrating 25 years of the Chilterns Chalk Streams Project', https://www.chilternstreams.org/.

time. I realised a lot of high-quality drinking water, up to 50 litres a day, is flushed down the toilet. 'Wet, lather, rinse' uses less water than a continual shower or tap flow and cleans more effectively. There was greywater that could be captured from the shower. Did I really need to shower daily in winter? (Indigenous peoples in cold climates don't.) How long did the shower need to be? Did the toilet have to be flushed? Following the example of permaculture experts, I peed into bottles of greywater to feed garden plants and composting. It can be ideal.[96]

When I got the next water bill (Fig.4), the results were dramatic. My water use had plunged over half, by 58%, from a daily **117 litres** in the first six months of 2020 to just **49 litres** for the same period in 2021. I sustained this in 2022. My use was 32% of average daily use in the South East (152 litres) and 35% of the national average (141 litres). That I could so without any new technology, without discomfort, and with no complaints about my personal hygiene (!) proved to me that significant reduction in domestic water use is possible. The use accords with UN estimates that 50 litres a day is adequate if water is not required for flush toilets.[97]

Although my water bills fell by about a third, £5 a month, that didn't reflect the scale of savings. Fixed charges accounted for 73% of the bill. So, on behalf of 'eco-warrior water savers' everywhere I made a formal complaint to Affinity, my water company. To their credit they replied promptly and acknowledged that the standard charge did seem high, but said that they 'are currently calculated and apportioned equally through our customer base so each property contributes the same amount'. Superficially that sounds 'fair', but it needs challenging.

....

96 Redemption Permaculture, 'What is urine permaculture?'. https://redemptionpermaculture.com/what-is-urine-permaculture-find-out-here/.

97 The Conversation, 'The world needs more toilets – but not ones that flush', 21 March 2017. https://theconversation.com/the-world-needs-more-toilets-but-not-ones-that-flush-74007. .

Figure 4. Copy of Water Bill. July 2021

Affinity Water
Your local supply, on tap

SAS 96
1A 1D 1F

LIVE/2120701_09/102BI3/35800/4510/21303/1-2/101000

Mr T Hagyard

Visit us at **affinitywater.co.uk**
or call us on 0345 357 2401
Monday–Friday, 8am–6pm. Saturday, 8am–2pm.

Need help reading this? Turn to the last
page of this bill.

	Your customer number	
	Your meter number	
	Bill date	31 July 2021
	Clean water emergency?	0345 357 2407
	Waste water emergency?	0800 316 9800
	This bill is for your water supply to	

Here's your water bill

You used

9,000 litres

from 22 Jan 2021 to 28 Jul 2021

That's around **49 litres** of water
every day – that's less than **1
bathtub.**

Thank you – you're using 76.67% less
water than similar-sized water-efficient
households in your neighbourhood.

Keep reading for handy tips on how to
save water, save money, and help take
care of our local area.

We'll collect monthly payments of

£11.00

over the next 7 months

You don't need to do anything.

We'll take **£11.00** on **1 Sep 2021**, then collect
£11.00 payments by Direct Debit on the **1st** of
each month after that.

See **page 2** for a full breakdown of your bill →

Thanks for paying by Direct Debit

It's the easiest and fastest way to pay.

We'll continue to collect your payments, and you
won't need to lift a finger.

Doughnut tariffs

Fuel poverty as energy costs rise is widely recognised, if not well addressed. Water poverty is less acknowledged but is also a reality in the UK. The National Audit Office has reported that water bills have increased 40% since privatisation, and that water costs have risen more steeply for poorer households. While the richest 10% spend about 1% of their household income on water bills, the poorest 10% spend over 5% of their income. A proportion of 3% is considered the threshold for water poverty.[98]

So perhaps 12% of customers, 2 million, find their water bills unaffordable. There are currently various 'social tariffs' designed to reduce charges for up to 500,000 customers, but they're too limited and patchy. The Consumer Council for Water recommends a single social tariff. High and rising standing charges are happening in energy use too, so low-income households are impacted by price rises even as they reduce use of fuel. In the six months to April 2022, energy standing charges increased by 50%. We clearly need more effective social tariff pricing to help the poorest.[99]

A good tariff can tier prices in blocks so that the price increases at varying thresholds of use. This happens in Flanders, Belgium where average water use is only 104 litres a day. Access to clean water is recognised internationally as a human right,[100] so it is right that everyone receives water to meet their basic essential needs at nil or minimal charge. Then there's the 'polluter pays' principle. The tariff can price in environmentally damaging high water use, recognising that excessive water use is in itself a form of pollution. What would you call pricing

98 National Energy Action 2020, Water Poverty: The Consistency of Social Tariffs. https://www.nea.org.uk/wp-content/uploads/2020/10/Water-Poverty-The-Consistency-of-Social-Tariffs.pdf.

99 Izabel Bahia, 'What you need to know about your energy bill and the cap', 12 August 2022. https://policyinpractice.co.uk/what-you-need-to-know-about-your-energy-bill-and-the-cap/.

100 United Nations, 'Human rights to water and sanitation'. https://www.unwater.org/water-facts/human-rights-water-and-sanitation.

that radically drives both ecological and social objectives at the same time? Eco-social tariffs? A WWF report called them amended IBTs.[101] I contemplated 'harmonic tariffs', conducive to harmony both in society and in our relationship with nature. But 'doughnut tariffs' would be best (I explain later). Here is an example of how tiered pricing for water use might be structured, although precise bands may need more evidence-based work, and allowances would be added for children and disabled people to cover personal needs.

- 0–80 litres pppd   zero or minimal charge

- 80–110 litres pppd   low charge

- 110–150 litres pppd   higher charge

- Above 150 litres pppd   excess use charge

  (pppd = per person per day)

The block threshold proposed in the example reflects the fact that 80 litres a day is a reasonable aspiration for a developed European country, and has been achieved in Denmark. A total of 110 litres is Ofwat's and the Water Industry's agreed target for average use. On the other hand, 150 litres represents the current highest average use levels. Above 150 litres a day, excessive use, would be charged accordingly as an incentive to economise and invest in water efficiency.

Affinity identifies 9% of its customers as 'super low' users below 110 litres a day – most of these will live in smaller homes or apartments without a garden. The Water Industry knows that consumption increases for larger detached houses, homes with gardens and swimming pools.

---

101 World Wildlife Fund, *Waste Not, Want Not: Sustainable Water Tariffs*, 2007. http://assets. wwf.org.uk/downloads/water_tariffs_report01.pdf.

Affinity's latest Water Resource Management Plan revealed that 22% of customers use over 300 litres a day.[102] Clearly there are big savings to be made here. Without any behaviour changes or water-saving investment, bills at the high user end would rise significantly with such tariffs. Affinity considered but rejected 'tariff strategies', saying they would be difficult to price and may impact on vulnerable customers. It also implied that the highest users are so wealthy that pricing has no impact on their behaviour. I doubt that. Even if it's the case, at least the polluter pays and the poorest get a significant cross-subsidy and much more help than at present.

In contrast to Affinity's view, the draft (October 2021) of the CaBA Coalition Chalk Stream Restoration Strategy viewed tariffs very positively:

Metering with appropriate tariff structures – such as the rising block tariff (where the unit charge rises for progressively higher volumes of water taken by customers), or a seasonally-varying or aridity-indexed tariff (where water costs more per unit when it is less plentiful) – has the potential to be a major incentive for water efficiency in the future. Should the water that someone fills a swimming pool with really cost as little as the water everyone else makes a cup of tea or washes their hands with? [103]

....

102 Affinity Water published a draft Water Resources Management Plan 2024 in Nov 2022. It aims to reduce average consumption from 157 to 136 litres a day by 2050. https://affinitywater.uk.engagementhq.com/wrmp.

103 *CaBA Chalk Stream Restoration Strategy* October 2021, https://catchmentbasedapproach.org/learn/chalk-stream-strategy-3/

A difficult but necessary approach

In her groundbreaking book *Doughnut Economics*,[104] Kate Raworth destroys the bankruptcy of much orthodox economic theory and posits a new economics to secure a just and stable future, living within the earth's planetary limits and addressing essential social needs. 'The Doughnut' is the space we need to live in, between two concentric rings – an outer ring that is our 'ecological ceiling' and an inner ring which secures a 'social foundation'. Harmonic or 'doughnut' tariffs would be a form of utility pricing that aligns with this approach. It takes us into that doughnut space where we meet people's essential needs for water while respecting the finite environmental capacity of the planet.

Given the social and environmental benefits, I suspect 'doughnut' or tiered tariff pricing has a wider applicability in areas beyond water and energy, such as transport and housing. However, it requires quite bold decision-making and may not be popular with those who 'lose out', unless well explained and carefully introduced. For water, it could radically support the poorest with their bills reflecting their lower levels of use. It would also incentivise affluent excess users, the polluters, to adapt. Those with a private swimming pool, attached to frequent baths or long power showers (60–80 litres) may balk at extra charges, but at least the pricing would reflect the environmental cost. The better-off are also more able to invest in rainwater capture, water butts, rainwater tanks, water reuse and other water-efficient technologies. Tariff pricing would automatically and systematically moderate the kinds of activity, hose pipe use in gardens for instance, that companies and politicians are so reluctant to restrict even during extreme droughts.

As Raworth herself explains, pricing in itself has its limits and is no substitute for embedded shared values about essential commodities such as water. Reflecting on the life-affirming preciousness of water,

....
104 Kate Raworth, *Doughnut Economics: Seven Ways to Think Like a 21st-Century Economist.* Penguin Books, 2017.

reducing waste was incentive enough for me and I think it would be for most people. Of course, living as a single person, working part-time, with no young children or large garden, my circumstances are far from typical. Pricing needs to reflect the true value of water but given that people are busy, with many daily demands and decisions, we need conservation built into our water management systems as the default option as well as into our habits and values. Hamburg in Germany for example is progressing systems[105] that separate at source blackwater, greywater and rainwater and also generate energy and fertiliser as a by-product. Eddington in Cambridge is a good UK example of a housing development that separates rain and surface water run-off for reuse. These systems also help to radically reduce water use.

Using less of anything is not a message politicians readily adopt. It's partly the unquestioned mantra of limitless 'growth' which has brought us to where we are. It's also true that the poorest sections of society shouldn't be using less than they need in any event. Politicians see restraint as 'anti-aspirational' and a vote loser. Yet when this attitude is cultivated, it's our environment and the planet that pays the price. Rivers and aquatic life don't get a vote. It's a key reason we haven't taken far more robust climate action – behavioural change is one of the hardest areas for political leadership. No one likes to be told to change; it risks charges of hypocrisy or a 'nanny state'. I also think it would be much more difficult to sell doughnut tariffs with a retained privatised water industry. The losers will point to profiteering, high salaries and bonus payments while water companies fail to address leaks or meet water quality standards. Nonetheless it appears Ofwat and other water companies are considering a more exacting tariff system.[106]

....
105 'The Hamburg Water Cycle® in the Jenfelder Au', https://www.hamburgwatercycle.de/the-hwc-in-the-jenfelder-au.html.
106 Helena Horton, 'Britons who do not pave over garden could receive water bill discount', The Guardian, 28 March 2023. https://www.theguardian.com/environment/2023/mar/28/uk-water-saving-bills-ofwat.

19. All things are connected: water care, water use and river restoration

Walking the rivers of Hertfordshire was by turns delightful and unsettling. It wasn't all doom and gloom. I saw healthy chalk streams and fine river restoration projects, and learned of the many 'friends of the river ...' groups. In a sentence, what would I wish for now?

Ecologically wild and healthy rivers, where nature thrives, clean and safe for swimming, within accessible public corridors.

The chalk streams of Hertfordshire and England are an international asset. We hear politicians boast that we are 'world beating'. Well, our chalk streams certainly should be, so let's get our own house and rivers in order. I think the collaborative multi-agency plan within the CaBA Chalk Stream Restoration Strategy October 2021[107] and Implementation Plan, November 2022, sets out a way to do that. It needs cross-party-political backing and resourcing. It is built around the 'trinity of ecological health': water quality, water quantity and habitat quality. Here are my own 'chalk stream reflections' on these three key elements.

---

107 CaBA Chalk Stream Restoration Strategy and Implementation Plan, November 2022, https://catchmentbasedapproach.org/learn/chalk-stream-strategy-3/

1. Water care (water quality)

The public interest and a culture of care

Regrettably, the current national picture on river health and cleanliness is really quite poor. The UK ranks last in Europe for the quality of its bathing water.[108] Environment Agency data published in 2020 confirmed river quality had deteriorated since 2016. No rivers, lakes or streams are now classed as being in 'good health' in England. And previously it was only 16%. Under the 2003 EU Water Framework Directive, the government originally set a legal target of 2015 for all waters to be in 'good health'. This target was pushed backed repeatedly to 2027 and now has disappeared altogether.

Failing sewage treatment has become headline news. There is a lot of damage already from nutrients such as phosphorus in treated water. Compounding this are 'storm overflows' of untreated sewage. In 2019, an Environment Agency report revealed 1.5 million hours of untreated sewage were poured into UK rivers. DEFRA figures showed this increased to 2.7 million hours in 2021 then reduced to 1.75 million in 2022. These figures are alarming and unprecedented. In Hertfordshire, there were over 1,000 spills in 2021 for a duration of 15,000 hours.[109] Prosecution looks ineffectual. In 2022 there were only 20 prosecutions, compared with 200 back in 2012. There was a reduction of a third in river enforcement staff between 2012 and 2017. Prosecutions are lengthy and costly for the regulators and fines are small relative to water company profits. In 2019, four water companies paid £1.3m in

108 Max Colbert, 'Why British bathing water is the dirtiest in Europe', Byline Times, 6 December 2022. https://bylinetimes.com/2022/12/06/the-sewage-scandal-the-worst-we-have-seen-in-years-why-british-bathing-water-is-the-dirtiest-in-europe/.

109 CPRE Hertfordshire, 'Latest raw sewage figures: what's in Hertfordshire's waterways?', 19 June 2022. https://www.cpreherts.org.uk/news/latest-raw-sewage-figures-whats-in-hertfordshires-waterways/.

fines,[110] which amounted to about 2p for every £100 of profit. Judges give damning verdicts on deliberate negligence by companies. These are decisions from the top not operational accidents, yet the spilling persists.

The UK also has a legacy of combining wastewater[111] that mixes foul sewers with rainwater and surface run-off. The Government Taskforce says it would cost between £350 billion and £600 billion to eliminate storm overflows, while campaigners dispute this. Fears of system overload in heavy rains is given as the reason for the sewage spills (the government and industry prefer the term 'storm overflows') but this does not explain why spills have increased so dramatically since 2016. Campaigners cite evidence of abuse. It seems more likely that the threat of legal action has receded and it's just cheaper to spill as well as to underinvest in treatment works capacity.

We need a transformation in the outlook of government, the water industry and water regulators to meet the challenges and context of ecological and climate crises. We should abandon the idea that water be run as a business and 'pay its way'. Like health and education, it's far too important for that. A 'revolving door' of appointments between water companies and regulators feeds fears that they themselves have been captured by a commercial mindset. We need a **'culture of care'** that's embedded from top to bottom, giving first priority to river health and ecology. Many believe the answer is to take water companies back into public ownership, as is the case in Scotland, Europe and most developed countries. Improvement isn't guaranteed by public ownership, but it's hard to see how the culture would change without moving away from an industry now immersed in profit maximisation, high executive pay and bonus culture.

110 Sandra Laville, 'England's privatised water firms paid £57bn in dividends since 1991', *The Guardian*, 1 July 2020. https://www.theguardian.com/environment/2020/jul/01/england-privatised-water-firms-dividends-shareholders.
111 Environment Agency, 'Combined sewer overflows explained', July 2020. https://environmentagency.blog.gov.uk/2020/07/02/combined-sewer-overflows-explained/.

It is claimed companies have been paying out three times more in dividends than they are spending on investment.[112] Our water companies are natural monopolies, making millions in profits for shareholders.[113] There is justifiable public distrust and a level of genuine anger. As companies fail, calls have been made for jail terms for directors, a ban on bonuses for chief executives, a public commission or inquiry into water regulation.

The 1989 privatisation of the England and Wales ten regional water authorities was a controversial step. There was new investment, but accumulated debts of £45bn since then mean higher costs for consumers. Bills are 40% higher in real terms since 1989.[114] Improvements to beaches were driven as much by EU legal directives and sanctions which didn't depend on privatisation. Polls clearly say renationalise.[115]

Reinstating the resources for regulation would help, whatever the ownership. The National Rivers Authority, forerunner of the Environment Agency (EA), averaged over 7,000 enforcement visits a year up to 1995. In 2019 the number of EA visits was merely 300. We need effective robust government regulation, but the authorities are 'missing in action' as citizen scientists and local campaigners struggle to plug the gaps. In Hertfordshire, as elsewhere, private cesspits, farms and local treatment works need regular checking. Public investment in

---

112 C4 Dispatches, *Britain's Water Scandal*, August 2022.

113 Sandra Laville, 'England's privatised water firms paid £57bn in dividends since 1991', *The Guardian*, 1 July 2020. https://www.theguardian.com/environment/2020/jul/01/england-privatised-water-firms-dividends-shareholders.

114 National Audit Office, *The Economic Regulation of the Water Sector*, October 2015. https://www.nao.org.uk/reports/the-economic-regulation-of-the-water-sector/.

115 In 2017 an opinion poll stated 59% of the British public (78% of those who had a view) favoured renationalisation of all water services. https://yougov.co.uk/topics/politics/articles-reports/2017/05/19/nationalisation-vs-privatisation-public-view.

In 2022 69% were in support. 78% of those who had a view said it should be renationalised. https://www.survation.com/new-poll-public-strongly-backing-public-ownership-of-energy-and-key-utilities/.

Hertfordshire's treatment works should prioritise large works such as at Luton, Letchworth and Chesham, which are close to river headwaters and where the impacts of contamination are all the greater.

I think the strongest case for removing the profit element is that future water use and demand management needs full public trust and co-operation. A nationalised, municipalised or a non-profit company/charitable trust could hope to win over the public to water conservation. Looking around the world, it seems no small coincidence that Copenhagen and Singapore, two cities with some of the best track records on water conservation, have publicly owned water supplies.

Public access and water quality

Some landowners resist increased public access. Countryside managers may prefer exclusion of the public to give nature some wilderness and avoid other problems. I recall discussions that Panshanger Park near Hertford should limit public access, although the popularity and public benefits of wider access seem fully accepted. There is a balance to be struck, to avoid disturbance of wildlife habitats, particularly at nesting times. The question of access to the countryside, like access to rivers and right to roam, is beyond the scope of this book, although I have made chapter recommendations for local improvements. Overall, promoting rivers for health, nature appreciation and recreation, and as sustainable movement corridors, is good 'in principle' and I support those advocating for far greater public access to rivers.[116] Public education and responsibility are needed too, but look at the educational value of a place like the Amwell Reserve. With increased public access comes understanding, appreciation and scrutiny. It worked for me.

....
116 Nick Hayes, *The Book of Trespass: Crossing the Lines That Divide Us*, Bloomsbury, 2020, estimates only 3% of rivers have unrestricted public access.

'The world reveals itself to those who travel on foot'

(**Werner Herzog**)

Hertfordshire groups have been instrumental in delivering valued walks such as the River Ver Trail and the Chess Valley Walk. I look forward to others in the county such as a Mimram or Gade Valley Walk, or a Rhee to Cambridge Trail. During the restrictions of the pandemic people explored local green spaces and rivers far more and noticed for themselves that nature isn't thriving. Nationally, only 3% of our rivers are accessible to the public and in Hertfordshire I suspect the figure is not much higher. This limits swimming opportunities. In France and Germany, access to inland bathing is far higher at 38% and 84%.

The river Wharfe at Ilkley was the first river site in the UK to enjoy bathing status,[117] and it has increased awareness of water quality with weekly monitoring and testing. In Britain, Surfers Against Sewage have a campaign for 200 river bathing waters to be designated by 2030 (there are 500 in France). In Hertfordshire, I look forward to many designated swimming sites, such as at Aldenham Reservoir, the Gade at Cassiobury Park, Stanborough Lakes Welwyn or the Kingsmeads on the Lea.

River access and river swimming would be a good local indicator for our collective well-being. So, head out, explore your rivers and demand new routes and better public access. River corridors often provide the best way to travel between nearby places and new routes can help enliven the riversides in the centre of our towns and villages.

2. Water use (quantity)

Our excessive use of water for agriculture, industry and domestic purposes is a major reason our rivers are depleted in water quantity and flow. High domestic consumption is particularly a factor in heavily

....
117 Ilkley Clean River Group, https://ilkleycleanriver.uk/.

populated and water-stressed Hertfordshire. Water conservation can build greater resilience of supply as we adapt to climate change. It also reduces our carbon footprint given the energy used treating and transferring water. The UK Committee on Climate Change has said demand reduction in water use is critical.

My own experiment convinced me of the possibility to save more and the potential benefits of (doughnut) tariffs. I'm sure pricing for social and environmental objectives has applicability in other areas such as transport, energy and even housing. It accords with the 'doughnut economics' expertly espoused by Kate Raworth. Water companies and providers of infrastructure may argue it's fair that everyone pays a flat rate charge, but that is not far away from the logic of the failed 1980s poll tax. More importantly it is not 'regenerative or redistributive by design' as Raworth advocates so doesn't tackle water poverty or the unsustainable use of water.

Leakage

Leakage from our ageing water infrastructure is an important issue, but it shouldn't be used to deflect from water conservation. The National Audit Office 2020 noted the lack of progress on reducing leakage. Ofwat estimate that 20% of water is lost in leakage.[118] In England that's about 3 billion litres or 50 litres per person a day. Ofwat demand reductions to leaks while pointing out that performance is comparable with several other countries. Water UK rightly acknowledge that 'Customers do not like leakage because it is seen as inefficient, and a barrier to asking customers to conserve water'.[119] Their route map proposes savings by 2030 of 1 billion litres a day and a further 0.5 billion by 2050. Affinity Water, like other companies, in its latest Water Resource Management

118 Ofwat, 'Leakage in the water industry', 21 November 2022. https://www.ofwat.gov.uk/leakage-in-the-water-industry/#leakage1.
119 Water UK. A Leakage Route Map. 2022 https://www.water.org.uk/publication/a-leakage-routemap-to-2050/

Plan adopts the target to halve leakage to about 10% by 2050 but says beyond that would be too costly and increase water bills.[120]

nvestment is needed but when cost arguments are raised, the suspicion is that the industry is protecting shareholders and profit margins. Savings on leaks would demonstrate that the water industry, whether it's private or public, is 'playing its part'. You can't ask individuals to economise and change behaviour when the system itself is so wasteful. In Singapore, seeking to be water independent, they reduced leakage to a world record low of 5%, using smart valve sensors which listen for leaks that elsewhere go undetected for months. The Plan for Water in the UK says artificial intelligence and drones can be used to detect leaks. Far greater urgency, ambition and investment is needed given the waste and the potential upsides.

Loss of water evaporating from surfaces is also an issue to consider. Worldwide about 5% of surface water is lost to evaporation. Lake Nasser in Egypt, 300 miles long, is an extreme example and estimated to lose 25–40% of the Nile's flow. With global heating, evaporation will become more significant for cooler climates such as the UK. The beauty of replenishing our chalk aquifers, permitting only sustainable use (< 10% of rainfall recharge), is that no water is lost from them to evaporation. They are natural storage systems. Rainwater tanks and water butts also have this built-in resilience. It might change the cost–benefit appraisal of new infrastructure such as reservoirs and channels compared to water conservation and demand management.

Metering

There is a growing campaign chorus to introduce universal metering as soon as possible, not just for households but for private abstractors too. This is common in developed countries. Currently about 60% of UK

120 Affinity Water. *Draft Water Resources Management Plan* 2024 , Nov 2022. https:// affinitywater.uk.engagementhq.com/wrmp

homes are metered[121] with the rest having no price incentive to limit or reduce their use. Most business abstraction licences are unmetered too. Why do we accept this for such a precious resource? The WWF back in 2009[122] sought full water metering by 2020, observing that those metered reduced their consumption by 10–15%. EA studies show that water meters led to a 22% reduction in household water use.[123] Affinity plan to increase metering in their area to 75% by 2025. They advised me that 70% of people who switch to a meter save money.

Being metered gave me valuable information on my own water use challenge. If I'd had live 'smart metering' of my water use, the instant feedback would have been a further inducement. If 'doughnut' eco-social tariffs are introduced, live meters would help consumers keep track of their use to stay within a certain pricing band, perhaps aiming for free basic use as a reward for their efforts. Live meters can also help to highlight domestic water leaks from taps or dual flush toilets.

It's a resource not waste water

In Pakistan, around 2500 BC, at Mohenjo-Daro, one of the first human civilisations brought sanitation, civility and better public health to the city by provision of brick toilets over a sewer system that washed waste to a cesspit outside the boundaries. The Greeks, Romans and others also employed sanitation systems to discharge human waste elsewhere. With lower populations the consequences weren't probably so damaging. Modern flushing toilets began to arrive when 650,000 people 'spent a

....
121 Smart metering in draft water resources management plans UK Government Published 22 June 2023 https://www.gov.uk/government/publications/a-review-of-englands-draft-regional-and-water-resources-management-plans/appendix-a-smart-metering-in-draft-water-resources-management-plans
122 World Wildlife Fund, *Rivers on the Edge*, 2009. http://assets.wwf.org.uk/downloads/rivers_on_the_edge.pdf.
123 WaterWise, 'The effects of the universal metering programme on water consumption, welfare and equity', 2019. https://database.waterwise.org.uk/knowledge-base/the-effects-of-the-universal-metering-programme-on-water-consumption-welfare-and-equity-2019/

penny' in a first public facility at the Crystal Palace Great Exhibition of 1851. Legislation in 1848 requiring WCs in new homes popularised them but the increased use of water then overloaded local cesspits, culminating in London's infamous 'Great Stink' of 1858. Parliament could no longer ignore the issue and a modern city sewer system was constructed. The adoption of flushing systems for cities is international. We are strongly conditioned to 'flush and forget'. However, wet water systems increase water use several-fold and are unsustainable. As the writer Fred Pearce observes, the world needs to go on potty training[124] and start once again viewing sewage as a resource. We need systems that separate in the way Hamburg is doing to create energy and fertiliser and to recycle water. We need reliable dual flush toilets, vacuum toilets, waterless urinals, natural filtration, sprinkler taps and dry compost loos where feasible. All should be incentivised and invested in. The concept of 'waste' has to change, reflecting the principles of the 'circular economy' and the workings of natural ecosystems.

Respecting the value of water

While addressing leaks, metering and doughnut price tariffs all help, the greatest driver for change could be public attitudes. That basic desire to do the right thing. Intuitively I believe we all feel that connection, whether it's spiritual or scientific, to the life-affirming properties of water for ourselves and for nature. Fifty years ago, we used to throw all 'rubbish' into landfill. It's shocking when you think about it now. Look at the efforts of people, not least the young, to recycle. I'm sure the same thing will happen as people are more mindful of water use and connect it to the health of their local wildlife, rivers and outdoor bathing sites.

---

124 Fred Pearce, When the Rivers Run Dry: The Global Water Crisis and How to Solve It. Granta Publications, 2018.

Figure 5. Restoring Chalk Streams

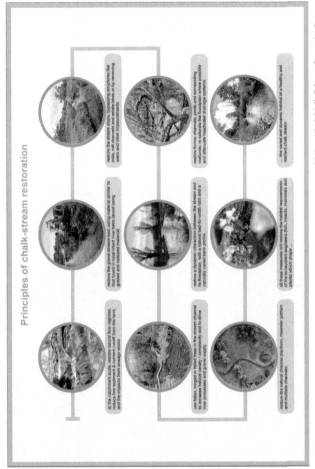

Principles of chalk-stream restoration

restore the stream slope, bypassing structures like mills, and channels and structures or by removing weirs and other impoundments

restore former channels, pools and surrounding wetlands; re-saturate the floodplain where possible and attenuate headwater drainage systems

...the varied and dynamic habitat of a healthy and resilient chalk stream

restore the gravel stream-bed, using material similar to that found in local intact river beds (avoid using graded and outsized material)

restore a dynamic interaction between the stream and its floodplain, with a natural bed-to-width ratio and a naturally varied bank profile

all these measures will restore the habitat requirements of the ecosystem engineers (fish, insects, mammals and plants) which shape ...

at the catchment scale, restore natural flow regimes, reduce fine sediment & nutrient runoff from the land, and the impacts from sewage works

use fallen, hinged or felled trees in the stream channel to increase habitat variety / complexity and to drive river processes and gravel supply

restore the natural channel platform, meander pattern and multiple channels

3. *River restoration (habitat)*

Restore, rewild and regenerate. I initially assumed most damage to our chalk streams was due to over-abstraction and the amount of pollutants being discharged into them. With the walk and subsequent research, I learned how important the physical form of rivers is. In fact, CaBA's coalition of experts says it's the most important factor. The Government Plan for Water 2023 rates it as the most significant issue. The fact that we aren't aware of this is partly our being so conditioned to the current man-made landscape and countryside.

CaBA with the Rivers Trust, Wildlife Trusts, Wild Trout Trust, Wild Fish Conservation and River Restoration Centre have endorsed a statement of 'principles for chalk stream restoration as a benchmark for work' (Fig 5). Over millennia, human societies increasingly moved to control rather than work with nature and to control water for private gain. This saw ever more engineering of the environment with land drainage, loss of wetlands, ditch digging and dredging to create rapid run-off channels, the diversion of water for mills and canals, hard culverting, weirs and reservoirs etc. It's still going on and the intensively managed South East was hugely affected. Chalk streams have an intrinsically gentle nature, but as calming and beautiful as they can be, they do not have the power to self-repair if just left to themselves. So, we need to learn soft engineering skills that restore them as close to the natural forms of the post-glacial era as possible.

As a society we must deliver long-term funding for river restoration as knowledge, skills and experience grow. Restoration incorporates much of the understanding that underpins sustainable drainage systems, which have long been advocated but often left as a 'nice to do' voluntary option. Public funds for flood alleviation should embrace natural flood management but it's not clear if this will work in practice or if the capacity is there. The Catchment Restoration Fund[125] of £24m enabled forty local restoration projects between 2012 and 2015. In 2016, Defra announced £15m for natural flood management schemes. More funding is to be resourced by water companies as they scope out action. The Plan for Water 2023 announced a Water Restoration Fund channelling the environmental fines and penalties imposed on water companies. This may be about £20m a year based on total fines of £141m since 2015. I seriously doubt this matches the scale of investment needed.

There is urgent and long-term work required as we adapt to more extreme rainfall patterns with climate change, notwithstanding many other benefits. The shift to restore is a pattern found in other countries. In 1995 the Dutch evacuated 250,000 people as the Rhine flooded. They changed their policy to 'Room for the River' and allocated a budget of 2.3 billion euros (£2bn). At Nijmegen, works on the river Waal created a new relief channel, and an urban living space as well as wetland habitat.[126] On the Loire in France, upstream dams were proposed then scrapped to create new meanders. In Seoul, South Korea and Utrecht, Netherlands they turned the clock back on culverted rivers and canals. Roads were closed and riverscapes reopened for wildlife and amenity. It's an idea to explore for the culverted river channel at Bishops Stortford.

In Hertfordshire, I came across exemplary restoration at Boxmoor on the river Bulbourne, Gadebridge on the Gade and Woodhall Park on the river Beane, where 130 water vole have been released to re-establish. The restoration of chalk streams in essence rewilds them, creating far richer habitats. The Environment Agency guidance on Natural Flood Management in 2021 gives 'medium level' confidence that restoration reduces flood risks. It slows water, reduces pollutants and helps to

....
125 *Catchment Restoration Fund: Environment Agency Summary Report* 2014 to 2015.
   https://www.gov.uk/government/publications/catchment-restoration-fund-environment-agency-summary-report-2014-to-2015.
126 Article by BaCA Architects' Eiland Veur Lent, Nijmegen, *Urban Design Journal*, Autumn 2015. https://www.udg.org.uk/publications/journal/urban-design-136-autumn-2015.

address risks of downstream flooding. Investment in Hertfordshire for chalk stream habitats will reduce flood risks in London and other towns downstream. Given the gains and the huge costs of flooding (£1.6bn in 2015/16),[127] the case is surely made for regular and more ambitious funding to build greater resilience. Restore away!

Conclusion

Times change but as a society we are still largely tied to consumerism and materialistic notions of growth. So, we continue to ignore the lessons of the Brandt Commission 1980, to live within ecological limits. Our approach to water and rivers will hopefully shift as part of a wider holistic approach to economy, the doughnut economics model being as good as any. We need to elevate the importance of well-being and regenerative growth, and abandon the dictates of measures such as Gross Domestic Product (GDP) and per capita consumption which are stealing the future and destroying the natural balance.

Avoid the persistent confusion of growth with development ... we strongly emphasise that the prime objective of development is to lead to self-fulfilment and creative partnership in the use of a nation's productive forces and its full human potential.[128]

The public want this for rivers. A coalition of bodies, including the RSPB, National Trust, Rivers Trust and Wildlife Trusts in 2021 published an opinion poll showing overwhelming support for higher standards. The *Troubled Waters* report set six key actions:[129]

---

127 UK Government, 'Counting the cost of flooding: improving evidence to inform funding and spending', 25 February 2021. https://www.gov.uk/government/news/counting-the-costs-of-flooding.

128 Independent Commission on International Development Issues, chaired by Willy Brandt, *North–South: A Programme for Survival*, 1980.

129 *Troubled Waters*, 2021. https://www.rspb.org.uk/globalassets/downloads/our-work/troubled-waters-report.

- systemic change to the planning approval system – integrate catchment-based decisions

- transition to regenerative farming practices and encourage sustainable nature-friendly eating

- legally binding targets for biodiversity and freshwater

- stop untreated sewage reaching our rivers

- sufficient resourcing of statutory agencies for robust monitoring and enforcement of existing policy and permits

- regularly monitor protected sites network to assess progress and target action where most needed

At Appendix A I have listed a range of ideas and actions including universal metering and a 'rights-based' approach to water charges. We have to review the ownership and priorities of the water industry. In Hertfordshire particularly we need regenerative farming practices across the chalk hills to care for and feed the aquifers, and we are seeing slow but tangible reductions in water abstraction with the prospect of more under a 'Chalk Streams First' policy. Hopefully we shall soon see the complete cessation of chalk groundwater abstraction in the upper parts of the Colne and Lea valleys.

In more pessimistic moments I see influential vested interests, short termism, political expediency, an almost wilful blindness, and inaction given the unimaginable challenges of ecological breakdown and climate change. But I tend to be optimistic. I have no doubt what the public's priorities are. In spite of the trajectory of climate forecasts and bad headlines on rivers, there is cause for hope. We can turn this around together.

One big reason for optimism is the work of campaigning coalitions, now embedded in far more holistic and science-based understanding of hydrological cycles and river management. Then there is the energy of grassroots groups. The love of nature is never more compellingly revealed than by the dedication of volunteers. Their voice is crying to be heard in the body politic and their energy feels like a tide waiting to burst the dam of orthodoxy, so that our streams once again flow wild and clean.

Let it be so.

'Then you don't promise never to touch a motor car again ? said the Badger.

Appendix A – Crunching the numbers on water

Water use, abstraction, leakage and charging

A clear idea of numbers helps one gain the right perspective. However, the plans and reports of water regulators and companies don't always make comparisons easy. The National Audit Office says 40% of total water abstracted is by farms, mills and others who source water directly; no methodology exists however for forecasting use beyond the water companies. Environment Agency whistleblowers say there is no reliable data to oversee these private abstraction licences, as they are mostly unmetered.

Agency areas

Water supply, wastewater responsibilities and regulation are fragmented and cover different administrative areas.

Hertfordshire is within the South East Region.

Affinity Water supply to most of Hertfordshire. Thames Water supply to a few small areas.

Thames Water manage most of Hertfordshire's wastewater. Anglian

Water manage wastewater from a few areas to the northern edge of Hertfordshire.

Ofwat is the national economic regulator of water companies.

The Environment Agency is the national agency responsible for water and river quality.

Domestic water use (average daily per person)

Chilterns (Hertfordshire)	174 litres
South East England	150 litres
Affinity Water customers	157 litres (reduced from 171 litres)
'Super low' users = 9% of customers	< 110 litres
'Super high' users = 22% of customers	> 300 litres
National	145 litres
Ofwat target (2050)	110 litres
Author's use (2020)	117 litres (fixed charge = 52% of water bill)
Author's use (2021–2)	49 litres (fixed charge = 73% of water bill)
Best practice	80 litres

(Eddington Cambridge, Copenhagen Denmark)

A doughnut tariff approach to water charging

0–80 litres pppd	zero or minimal charge
80–110 litres pppd	low charge
110–150 litres pppd	higher charge
Above 150 litres pppd	excess use charge

Principles

- Water is a precious resource. Excessive use equates to pollution, especially in water-stressed areas where biodiversity is highly vulnerable.

- Water is a basic human right. Help poorer low users with free basic provision. End fixed charges which disproportionately impact on the poor and are a disincentive to economise.

- Water supply and waste treatment should be run as an essential public and environmental service, not a business. Use general public funds to make up any shortfall in revenue (subject to review of banding).

- Universal metering and smart metering. Use pricing to help poorest and incentivise care and investment in water-saving technologies. Ensure the 'polluter pays'. Daily feedback on use helps educate and conserve.

Affinity Water Company Statistics (2023)

Supplies **950 million litres** a day (mld) of water to 3.8 million customers (250 litres each)

160 mld to non-household customers (17% of water)

65% of supply is abstracted from groundwater = **618 mld**

(The rest is from surface water sources at Iver, Egham, Walton, Chertsey (River Thames), Ardleigh (Brett) and a share of Grafham.)

Abstraction reduced from **716 mld** since 2003 (16% reduction)

2043 abstraction target of reduction to **520 mld**

70% of Affinity customers are metered (50% in 2012); target of 75% by 2025

(In UK 60% of households metered)

Metered households use 12% less water; majority of Affinity's non-household customers are metered

Leakage

189 mld leaking in 2015 = 21% of the supply

Aim to reduce 30% by 2025 to **148.5 mld**

Aim to halve leakage by 2050 to **95 mld** (approx. 10% of the supply)

Affinity argues costs of addressing leaks beyond the 50% reduction (10% of total supply) too great for customers

Daily domestic water consumption by activity

Essential

Drinking water	2–4 litres per person
Mixer eco shower 20–30 litres	(4 minutes)
Toilet flush	5–9 litres per flush (efficient dual flush: 4–6 litres / vacuum flush: 1.5 litres)
Washing machine	50–60 litres a cycle (8 litres a day per person)
Cooking / hand washing etc.	10–20 litres per person
Washing up / dishwasher	10–25 litres (4 litres a day per person)

Non-essential

Bath	60–80 litres
Power shower	52 litres (4 mins) – 78 litres (6 mins)
Paddling pool	400–3,000 litres
Private swimming pool	30,000–50,000 litres (daily: est. 250 litres)
Garden watering (hose)	200–500 litres (half an hour)
Car washing	250 litres (hose), 30 litres (bucket)

Questions for water use

- Can I shower rather than take a bath?
- Do I need to take a shower every day in winter?
- Do I leave the tap running while I wash my hands / brush my teeth?
- Can I capture water running for hot (or cold in hot weather)?
- Can I reuse water from shower to flush toilet?
- Do I need to flush the toilet?
- Can I harvest rainwater for the garden, washing cars or toilet flushing?

Appendix B – Positive actions and ideas for water and rivers

National policy

- National planning policy that invests in and regenerates run-down regions to divert **development pressures** away from water-stressed southern England. 'Regenerative development' which addresses social priorities, the finite limits of water and the harm to natural world by unsustainable 'extractive' development.[130]

- A **precautionary planning** approach that avoids major strategic development and increased demands on chalk streams, particularly for towns in upper catchment areas such as Letchworth and Baldock.

- Enact **Schedule 3** of the Flood and Water Management Act 2010. End automatic right of developers to connect into combined sewer system. Require SUDS in all new development. (Why was it delayed in England for over a decade?)

....
130 Current national definitions of 'sustainable development' have confused and discredited the term. Broadly speaking 'regenerative development' restores and repairs, while its antithesis would be 'extractive development' which consumes and exploits.

- Require all **new homes** to achieve minimum 110 litres per person per day and review with progressively more efficient targets.

- 'Slow the flow'. Incentivise retrofit provision of **SUDS** (Sustainable Urban Drainage) and rainwater harvesting in existing housing, commercial and built-up areas. Grant aid urban SUDS restoration schemes, and increase water charges and property rates related to the amount of water run-off/ hard surface area to incentivise free draining land.

- Ensure the **Environmental Land Management Schemes** (ELMS) for farmers in Hertfordshire and fund natural flood management that is aligned with the established principles of chalk stream restoration (Fig. 5).

- Review **Treasury Green Book** on cost–benefit analysis (designed for built infrastructure). For natural flood management it must value benefits of biodiversity, carbon sequestration, flood risk reduction, enhanced water quality and well-being.

- **End untreated discharges** of sewage into rivers by 2030 (see CPRE Herts and CPRE Oxfordshire response 12th May 2022)[131].

- Greater urgency and ambition to reduce **phosphorus levels in treated wastewater** (currently 50% by 2027) and use this as a nutrient resource for agriculture.

- Set up a **Citizens Assembly** alongside an independent **Commission** tasked to consider and make long-term

---

131 CPRE - The Countryside Charity Hertfordshire. Response on Storm Overflow Discharge Reduction Plan. https://www.cpreherts.org.uk/news/latest-raw-sewage-figures-whats-in-hertfordshires-waterways/

recommendations on all aspects of rivers, water use and management.

- Give Local Authority **Environmental Health** the resources and statutory duty to monitor and enforce ecological and environmental quality of waterways. With increasing swimming and river activity, like air quality and food safety which they cover, it's also a public health issue.

- A ban on non-biodegradable **wet wipes**. (Private Members' Bill by Labour MP Fleur Anderson.) These are clogging the sewers and we need re-educating as a nation.

- A ban on all but the essential use of '**forever chemicals**' – per- or poly-fluorinated alkyl substances (PFAS).[132] Stricter regulation and much better monitoring would be a great start to combating the harm that these chemicals cause.

- Committed long-term **Catchment Restoration Funds** to maintain knowledge and build capacity and skills of river restoration, rewilding and improved natural flood management.

- Designate all chalk streams in water-stressed areas SSSIs or create a new status, '**international priority habitat**', to recognise their globally unique nature with added protection.

....
132 Rivers Trust, https://theriverstrust.org/key-issues/chemical-pollution.

Leadership and governance

- Ministers for Environment, Water and Rivers to be appointed and remain for the **full Parliamentary term**. (We have had seven Secretaries of State for Environment in the last seven years). 'The main political parties and the civil service all agree that constant turnover of ministers is a core problem' [133]

- **Ministers** appointed preferably with some background expertise and knowledge, but with a commitment and determination to patiently stick to the task. Resisting the temptation for 'eye catching' initiatives or reliance on big spending announcements.

- Governments to show greater **continuity of good practice**. Acknowledge what their predecessors did which worked well and work with that too.

Ownership and management standards

- Move water companies into **public/municipal ownership** or move to non-profit charitable trust status. Profiteering has undermined public trust and willingness to co-operate with water conservation measures.

- **Clear ethos** of the water utilities/trusts to be set out – e.g. priority to climate adaptation, well-being and ecological health.

- **Groundwater abstraction** limited or ended in the upper parts of the Colne and Lea valley catchments. Within the range of a complete ban on abstraction in Source Water Protection

---

133 Institute for Government '*Government reshuffles The case for keeping ministers in post longer*'. Jan 2020. https://www.instituteforgovernment.org.uk/sites/default/files/publications/government-reshuffles.pdf

Zones to a manageable capture, 5–10% of the catchment recharge/effective rainfall.[134]

- **Replenish the chalk aquifers** to preserve and enhance a long-term resource which, unlike dams or reservoirs, doesn't lose water to evaporation.

- **Fit sensors** for early detection of leaks (as successfully done in Singapore). Water-stressed chalk stream areas such as Hertfordshire should be a funding priority.

Water charging

- End fixed standard charges and restructure pricing with **'doughnut tariffs'** (also for energy and other essentials like transport/property). A free or nominal 'essential use' tariff for basic water needs, e.g. up to 80 litres a day per person. Standard rates for up to 110 litres[135] a day per person. Higher charging rates for 'excess use' over 150 litres. Thresholds and pricing subject to monitoring of effectiveness and periodic review and lowering. To help those on lower incomes and incentivise care and conservation.

- Progress as rapidly as possible to **universal water metering**.[136] Demonstrated to reduce water use by 10–22%. Gradually raise charges on unmetered use. Roll out **smart metering**, in

....
134 *Celebrating 25 Years of the Chilterns Chalk Streams Project.* Chilterns Chalk Streams Project, 2022.
135 80 litres a day per person (lppd) has been achieved in Denmark. 110 lppd is the long-term target of Affinity Ofwat CaBA for 2050. 143 litres is average use. Some users are up to 300 lppd.
136 Recommendation in *Chalk Streams in Crisis* 2019 by a coalition of campaigning river and wildlife charities. Universal metering also recommended by National Infrastructure Commission, Committee on Climate Change, and the Environment, Food and Rural Affairs Parliamentary Committee. UK TAG guidelines are for no more than 5–10% of natural rainfall.

water-stressed areas as a priority. Estimated to reduce use by further 2%.

- Introduce **punitive fines** for water companies related to profits and quantity of pollution discharged (see Rivercide Emergency Rescue Plan).[137] While there are sewage discharges, if we can measure them make sure the polluter pays. This may only be an interim measure but could be done quickly.

- Universal metering of private groundwater abstraction licences to provide reliable data and ensure compliance.

Environment Agency

- Re-establish a properly funded **Rivers Unit** with staff enforcement levels returned to pre-2010 levels (Riverside call for a doubling of protection budgets).

- Re-naturalisation of the chalk stream morphology and flows to enhance biodiversity, amenity, water retention and pollution filtration.

- River flows to be restored and of sufficient quantity and quality to sustain key propagating fish species and allow swimming / bathing without risk to human health.

- Live public **display of pollution levels** for all key rivers (see Rivercide Emergency Rescue Plan).

- Identify **septic tank 'hot spots'** to raise standards and require tanks to meet a certifiable standard at point of property sale.

....
137 Rivercide, 'Emergency Rescue Plan: 5 things the government must do'. https://www.rivercide.tv/.

National Highways

- Enforce a review of all **highway stormwater** outlets with recommendations to capture pollutants by filtration upgrading of drains. Establish and fund a unit directly responsible for improvements to road run-off.

- A policy objective of **traffic reduction** and modal shift, to meet climate emission goals, reduce congestion and to reduce polluting road run-off, also produced by electric vehicles.

- A local **retail parking levy** (similar to the workplace parking levy[138]) to fund active and public transport. This could help rebalance out of town and in town retail, reduce traffic congestion and emissions and discourages large parking areas which increase flood risks and water run-off to combined sewers.

Local

- Set up a volunteer force of river **water quality monitors**. Train, accredit and fund via local environmental health teams. Work with existing 'Friends of the river …' groups (Rivercide – 'a standardised water sampling protocol so local citizens can collect polluted water for legal action').[139]

- Local 'Rights of Way' teams to include '**River Corridor Access' teams**. To proactively explore and improve opportunities for river corridor access for walking, running, cycling, swimming, nature watch and recreation. With core transport funding (i.e. not S106 handouts).

....

138 Meyer Brown Transport Consultants. 'The Growing Popularity of Workplace Parking Levies' November 2019. https://mayerbrown.co.uk/keep-up-to-date/blog/posts/the-growing-popularity-of-workplace-parking-levies/
139 Rivercide Emergency Rescue Plan. 5 things the government must do. https://rivercide.tv/

- Consistent multi-year funding of local action for **river restoration** with volunteer support. Restore natural river courses, morphologies and habitats where these have been straightened, culverted, engineered etc. – e.g. Boxmoor.

- Promotion of **regenerative agriculture** (see Groundswell) locally and nationally for benefits of nil-use of fertilisers and the benefits of rainwater capture across the chalk uplands of Hertfordshire.

- Buffer the banks. Make farm subsidies conditional on creating **wildlife corridors** along rivers and streams (see Rivercide Emergency Rescue Plan).

- Fund **PV roofs to cover all open manure** piles. Generate renewable energy while reducing water penetration and nutrient run-off.

Acknowledgements

Acknowledgements of thanks to Amos Trust who prompted the walk initiative. While following the rivers in Hertfordshire was my idea their work helps connect the local with the international issues of water, climate and social justice. Thanks to Will Parsons, Phil Hewett, Jim Coombes and Charles Rangeley-Wilson for their respective agreements to publish material within the book.

Thanks to all those who supported and walked the rivers of Hertfordshire with me, including Theo and Mariette Berkhout, Ken Coyne, Jenifer Ellis, Elisabeth Greenwood, Paul and Elisabeth Johnson, Alan Muhr, Lisa Page, Jane Wheeler and Ingrid Van Loo, for their company and conversation.

Special thanks to Elizabeth Hamilton at CPRE Hertfordshire for her early feedback, suggestions on reading material and advice with the approach on the overall narrative. Thanks too to those who helped review individual chapter content including Linda Brookes, Charles and Katy Bagnall, Ken Coyne, Jenifer Ellis, Mike Gilbert, Barbara Hopkin and Stephen Marcus.

I am honoured and delighted that Peter Ruffles, after 105 years of local government service as an elected Councillor with Hertford Town, East Hertfordshire District and Hertfordshire County Councils has written a foreword for the book. Thank you to Sara Magness for her editing and professional insights with the book content. To Mick Ashworth of Ashworth Maps for his advice on maps. To Andy Meaden for bringing it all together for a professional readable end product.

Finally, gratitude to all the hard-working volunteers in the local river friends groups, CPRE – The Countryside Charity, the Herts and

Middlesex Wildlife Trust and other environmental charities and trusts whose work I read about and witnessed on the walk and whose commitment inspired me to keep on writing.

Printed in Great Britain
by Amazon